UNIFORMITY OF CEMENT STRENGTH

A symposium
sponsored by
ASTM Committee C-1
on Cement
Louisville, KY, 19 June 1986

ASTM SPECIAL TECHNICAL PUBLICATION 961
Emery Farkas, W. R. Grace and Co., and
Paul Klieger, Portland Cement Association,
Editors

ASTM Publication Code Number (PCN)
04-961000-07

 1916 Race Street, Philadelphia, PA 19103

Library of Congress Cataloging-in-Publication Data

Uniformity of cement strength.

(ASTM special technical publication; 961)
"ASTM publication code number (PCN) 04-961000-07."
Includes bibliographies and index.
1. Cement—Testing—Congresses. I. Farkas, Emery.
II. Klieger, Paul. III. American Society for Testing and
Materials. Committee C-1 on Cement. IV. Series.
TA435.U57 1987   620.1′350287   87-17469
ISBN 0-8031-0961-X

NOTE

The Society is not responsible, as a body,
for the statements and opinions
advanced in this publication.

Printed in Ann Arbor, MI
September 1987

Foreword

This publication, *Uniformity of Cement Strength,* contains papers presented at the symposium of the same name held in Louisville, Kentucky, on 19 June 1986. The symposium was sponsored by ASTM Committee C-1 on Cement. Emery Farkas, W. R. Grace and Co., and Paul Klieger, Portland Cement Association, presided as symposium chairmen and were coeditors of this publication.

Related
ASTM Publications

Alkalies in Concrete, STP 930 (1986), 04-930000-07

Blended Cements, STP 897 (1986), 04-897000-07

Temperature Effects on Concrete, STP 858 (1985), 04-858000-07

Extending Aggregate Resources, STP 774 (1982), 04-774000-08

ASTM Journal *Cement, Concrete, and Aggregates*

A Note of Appreciation
to Reviewers

The quality of the papers that appear in this publication reflects not only the obvious efforts of the authors but also the unheralded, though essential, work of the reviewers. On behalf of ASTM we acknowledge with appreciation their dedication to high professional standards and their sacrifice of time and effort.

ASTM Committee on Publications

ASTM Editorial Staff

Contents

Overview

This symposium was organized to provide information on the impact of ASTM Method for Evaluation of Cement Strength Uniformity From a Single Source (C 917–82). This method is ". . . intended for use where the purchaser desires information on the strength uniformity of a hydraulic cement produced at a single source. It is intended that this method normally be used for the predominant cement manufactured at a cement plant."

The development of ASTM C 917 was the first step in an effort to improve the uniformity of concrete produced at a single source. Obviously, improvements in the uniformity (or, as might be stated, a decrease in the variability of the components used in concrete: cement, aggregates, and admixtures) would significantly aid in the concrete production process. Other production factors, of course, also play a role; concrete mixers, ambient conditions, weighing and batching equipment, etc. will continue to exert their influence and must also be considered.

The papers presented at this symposium provided the first approach to record in the literature the results achieved by the use of this relatively new ASTM standard, which was adopted in 1979 under the jurisdiction of ASTM Subcommittee C01.98 on Evaluating Cements for Uniformity. The use of this standard has been growing rather slowly since its adoption. It is hoped that the experiences described in this special technical publication will provide a stimulus for increased use so that further confirmation of the usefulness of this approach to one aspect of uniformity can be achieved.

As a result of the development of ASTM C 917 and its successful application, and despite its somewhat limited use to date, ASTM Committee C-1 on Cement and C-9 on Concrete and Concrete Aggregates have appointed a C-1/C-9 Task Group on Uniformity of Concrete-Making Materials. The Task Group will address the uniformity of aggregates, chemical admixtures, and materials such as fly ash in a manner similar to that for cement. The experiences described in this symposium should provide a useful example for this Task Group's activities.

While there is no substitute for a detailed reading of these reports, it may be helpful to describe each briefly. Oglesby reported on the development of a cement strength–testing program, based on ASTM C 917, adopted by the Illinois Department of Transportation. The major conclusion from efforts to date was that cement manufacturers are capable of furnishing cements which the user can be confident will vary in strength between known limits in the long run. Poole of the U.S. Army Waterways Experiment Station described experience with their Cement Quality Management System (CQMS), sufficiently similar to ASTM C 917 so that results can be evaluated by both methods. Their evaluation of 95 different portland cement sources indicated variability similar to that shown in the Appendix to ASTM C 917 and pointed to the importance of the type of sampling—24-h composite samples showed significantly less variation than grab samples. Al-Badr and Kilpadikar of the Saudi Kuwaiti Cement Manufacturing Co. presented a description of a modern and highly sophisticated cement plant in Saudi Arabia and attested to the use of ASTM C 917 as a ". . . suitable yard stick to assess whether the quality control procedures exercised are effective." Pielert and Spring of the Cement and Concrete Reference Laboratory (CCRL) at the U.S. National Bureau of Standards described the activities of CCRL with respect to cement testing, noting their efforts to increase the proficiency of testing by their proficiency sample programs, thus enhancing the reliability of test results obtained by the use of standards such as ASTM C 917. Taerwe of the Magnel Laboratory for Reinforced Concrete, Ghent State University in Belgium, described an approach to detect cement strength variations in a different manner than that proposed in ASTM C 917. The statistical approach used is a segmentation technique, that is, changes in mean strength level indicate a step-wise variation with time, rather than variation represented by a continuous curve. The objective, greater uniformity, is the same. Visvesvaraya and Mullick of the National Council for Cement and Building Materials, New Delhi, described the results of a 30-year survey of cement quality in India. Despite serious depletion of adequate raw materials and fuel supply problems, the monitoring of strength results has been a significant factor in maintaining the quality of production during this period.

In the final paper, Taryal and Chowdhury of the Saudi Arabian Standards Organization reported on studies of the variability of cement strengths in the eight companies in Saudi Arabia, using the Saudi standard test method, rather than ASTM C 917. Most of their report presented interesting data on changes in the test procedure and the resulting influence on strength variability measurements. The report concludes that the level of quality control is acceptable in all plants, although different among the eight plants.

The symposium was well attended and generated numerous questions directed to the speakers, testifying to the timeliness of the subject. It is hoped that continued use of ASTM C 917, in concert with activities of the C-1/C-9 Task Group on Uniformity of Concrete-Making Materials, will lead to a better understanding of the factors of importance to the production of uniform concrete.

Paul Klieger

P.O. Box 2275, Northbrook, Il 60065-2275;
symposium cochairman and editor

James R. Oglesby[1]

Illinois' Experience with Cement Strength Uniformity

REFERENCE: Oglesby, J. R., **"Illinois' Experience with Cement Strength Uniformity,"** *Uniformity of Cement Strength, ASTM STP 961,* E. Farkas and P. Klieger, Eds., American Society for Testing and Materials, Philadelphia, 1987, pp. 3–13.

ABSTRACT: The development of a cement strength uniformity requirement for the Illinois Department of Transportation's portland cement acceptance program is presented. The Department's historical test data indicate that while cement manufacturers have little difficulty producing cement meeting the minimum strength requirements of ASTM Specification for Portland Cement (C 150-85a), there is significant seasonal variation in strength for some manufacturers. Although cement strength variability is but one factor affecting concrete performance, it becomes of considerable practical importance in the design of economical concrete mixes. To determine the ability of manufacturers to produce cement of uniform strength, ASTM Method for Evaluation of Cement Strength Uniformity from a Single Source (C 917-82) test data was requested from each manufacturer furnishing cement to Illinois. Information on standard deviations, coefficients of variation, and 7- and 28-day average strengths is presented. The test information was studied, and a uniformity requirement was proposed wherein the manufacturer would submit 7- and 28-day strength levels at which he proposed to furnish cement, and control limits would be used to detect significant changes in the process average or variability. Information on standard deviations, coefficients of variation, and plots of average strengths are presented and compared to test information received before enforcement of the uniformity requirement. To verify test data reported by the manufacturer, split portions of selected ASTM C 917 samples are tested by the Department. Data obtained from these samples are also evaluated to determine differences in testing between the manufacturer and Department laboratories. The t-statistic is used to test whether the mean differences are significant. Data obtained are tabulated and presented. Results indicate that cement manufacturers are capable of furnishing cements which the user can be confident will vary in strength between known limits in the long run.

KEY WORDS: portland cement, compressive strength, standards, acceptance, variability, control limits

The Illinois Department of Transportation currently uses portland cement furnished by 17 cement manufacturing plants. Four plants are located in Illinois, four in Missouri, four in Michigan, three in Indiana, one in Iowa, and one in Kentucky.

Prior to July 1982, the Department routinely performed acceptance testing at each plant supplying cement to the State for highway construction. Commercial samplers obtained two random grab samples per day, five days per week, at each qualified plant. Sampling was accomplished as the cement was being transferred to the loading bins. The samples were mailed to the Department laboratory at Springfield, Illinois, and testing was performed in accordance with ASTM test methods. One of the two samples taken each day was tested for autoclave expansion and air content, and the other for strength and fineness. A random sample was selected for chemical testing approximately every three weeks. Qualified status for a plant was continued as long as results of the tests indicated compliance with the Department's critical limits.

[1]Cement technology engineer, Illinois Department of Transportation, Springfield, IL 62704-4766.

3

Historical Test Data

With few exceptions, cement received from these plants conformed to the requirements of ASTM Specification for Portland Cement (C 150-85a). However, a review of the Department's historical test data for compressive strengths showed that although the cement manufacturers had little difficulty in meeting the minimum strength requirements of ASTM C 150, plots of the strength data indicated significant seasonal variability for some manufacturers. Figure 1 shows a plot of the moving average of five for the 7-day mortar cube strengths obtained by the Department on random samples taken at one plant during 1981. (Prior to 1982, the Department tested only for 3- and 7-day strengths.) The plot shows large variability in strength within each quarter and a trend that begins with high strengths at the start of the year that gradually drops off during the construction months before rising again at the end of the year. Test data for this particular cement manufacturer showed that the range of the individual cube strengths was 1930 psi (13.3 MPa) with a minimum of 3300 psi (22.8 MPa) and a maximum of 5230 psi (36.1 MPa). Strength test data on samples from other cement sources showed similar variabilities and trends. Table 1 is a compilation of the 7-day strength results the Department obtained on random grab samples taken at the 15 plants furnishing cement to the State of Illinois in 1981. The results show that 40% of the plants had a strength range greater than 1600 psi (11.0 MPa), and 20% had a range greater than 1900 psi (13.1 MPa), and 67% of the plants had a total standard deviation less than 300 psi (2.1 MPa) for the entire year.

Cement strength variability is but one factor affecting concrete performance, but it becomes of considerable practical importance in the design of concrete mixes. Mixes using a cement of known strength and variability have an economic advantage over those which have to be designed to give comparable performance when using a cement certified to meet only the mini-

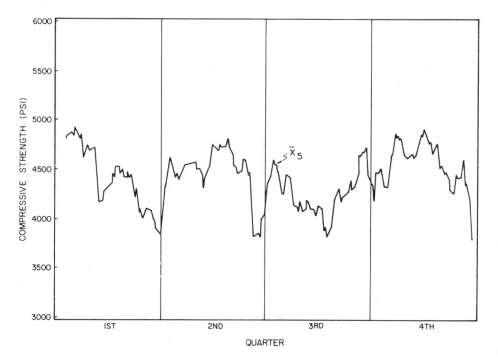

FIG. 1—*Moving average of five for C 109 mortar cube strengths at 7 days as tested by IDOT (1 psi = 0.0069 MPa).*

TABLE 1—*Summary of 7-day strength data for samples tested by the Illinois Department of Transportation (IDOT) in 1981.*

| Manufacturer | C-109 Compressive Strength, psi[a] | | | | | |
	Number of Tests	Average	Standard Deviation	Minimum Value	Maximum Value	Range
No. 2	261	4080	398	3060	5030	1970
No. 4	271	3840	258	3040	4750	1710
No. 5	171	4050	284	3220	4710	1490
No. 6	196	4340	247	3330	4880	1550
No. 7	252	4220	295	3550	5070	1520
No. 8	148	3950	292	3280	4720	1440
No. 9	258	3950	390	2960	6320	3360
No. 10	256	4170	265	3470	4930	1460
No. 11	239	3810	230	3190	4400	1210
No. 13	195	3660	289	2950	4460	1510
No. 14	183	3790	333	3020	4770	1750
No. 15	32	4200	281	3580	4780	1200
No. 17	246	4410	362	3300	5230	1930
No. 20	294	3900	307	3060	4690	1630
No. 21	129	3900	236	3330	4580	1250

[a] 1 psi = 0.0069 MPa.

mum ASTM strength requirements. Figure 1 indicates an instance where this advantage could not be realized since the large variability in strength over the year would require a contractor to allow for the possibility of receiving 3000 psi (20.7 MPa) cement, although the average is 4400 psi (30.3 MPa) and at times he is receiving 5000 psi (34.5 MPa) cement.

ASTM C 917

The elimination of funds for contract samplers in fiscal year 1983 required the Department to revise its cement sampling and testing program. The development of ASTM Method for Evaluation of Cement Strength Uniformity From a Single Source (C 917-82) afforded the Department an opportunity to reduce the amount of sampling and testing by the Department, to place more emphasis on acceptance of cement based on manufacturer tests, and to incorporate a strength uniformity requirement in its portland cement acceptance procedure. Since the manufacturers were required to obtain samples for their C 917 reports, the samples could conveniently be used to accomplish these objectives. In addition, testing of the same samples by the Department and by the manufacturer would detect any differences in testing that may occur between the two laboratories.

In early 1982, the Department requested C 917 test data from all producers furnishing cement to Illinois. Information on standard deviations, coefficients of variation, and 7- and 28-day average strengths is shown in Table 2. Of the seventeen manufacturers contacted, twelve responded but only eight were able to furnish enough test data to give an indication of the degree of strength variability in their shipments during 1981. Those eight manufacturers reported data for at least three quarters of the year and for at least ten samples per quarter. Table 2 shows that of the eight manufacturers, 75% reported a 7-day total standard deviation of less than 300 psi (2.1 MPa), and 38% reported less than 250 psi (1.7 MPa).

A review of the C 917 test data suggested that the judicious selection of an average target strength combined with a determined effort to improve quality control could result in more uniform shipments over the course of a year.

TABLE 2—*Summary of ASTM C-917 strength data reported to IDOT in 1981.*

	7-Day Compressive Strength, psi[a]				28-Day Compressive Strength, psi[a]			
Manufacturer	Number of Tests	Average	Standard Deviation	CV	Number of Tests	Average	Standard Deviation	CV
No. 2	62	4210	324	7.7	54	5680	328	5.8
No. 4	111	3890	173	4.4	111	4760	196	4.1
No. 5	87	4370	253	5.8	87	5760	258	4.5
No. 8	90	4260	256	6.0	90	6070	367	6.0
No. 10	45	4050	170	4.2	40	5170	184	3.6
No. 13	117	4110	252	6.1	117	5450	252	4.6
No. 17	76	4470	304	6.8	76	5900	357	6.1
No. 22	121	4410	206	4.7	115	5200	256	4.9

[a] 1 psi = 0.0069 MPa.

Uniformity Requirement

In July 1982, it was proposed that the 7- and 28-day strength data for Type I cement reported by the manufacturer be analyzed by the Department and the following control limits be used to detect significant changes in the process average or variability:

$$\text{Upper Limit} = \bar{\bar{X}} + 3s'/\sqrt{5}$$

$$\text{Lower Limit} = \bar{\bar{X}} - 3s'/\sqrt{5}$$

where:

$\bar{\bar{X}}$ = average 7- or 28-day strength at which the manufacturer proposes to furnish cement, and
s' = 250 psi.

A manufacturer was considered to be in compliance with the Department's uniformity requirement if not more than one moving average of five strength values fell outside the upper or lower limit in a given quarter (See Fig. 2). In order to give each manufacturer an opportunity to establish his target strengths, compliance with the uniformity provision was not required until January 1983. Following a meeting with the cement manufacturers to evaluate the results obtained in 1983, the value of s' used to calculate the upper and lower limits was changed from 250 psi (1.7 MPa) to 300 psi (2.1 MPa) on 1 Jan. 1984. It was decided that compliance with the uniformity requirement would be based on the 7-day strength results only. Compliance was not based on the 28-day test data as the results might be less objective. That is, if the 7-day results approached the upper or lower limit, there may be some incentive to influence the results of the 28-day test. Also, the results of the 7-day tests are known more quickly, and corrective action can be taken much sooner when problems do arise.

Statistical information obtained from the C 917 reports during the years 1981 through 1984 is presented in Tables 2 through 13. Tables 2 through 5 summarize the 7- and 28-day ASTM C 917 compressive strength data reported by cement manufacturers for the years 1981 through 1984. Data include the number of tests, average, total standard deviation, and coefficient of variation. Tables 6 through 13 give the cumulative percentages of manufacturers reporting 7- and 28-day strength total standard deviations less than various values.

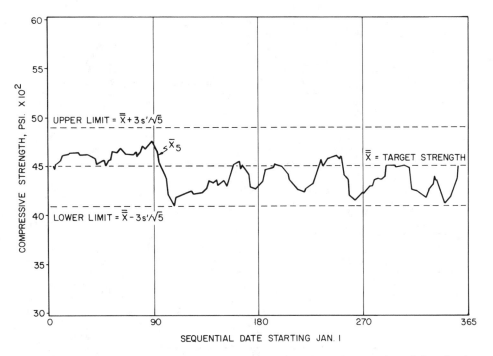

FIG. 2—*Control chart for moving average of five for C 109 mortar cube strengths at 7 days (1 psi = 0.0069 MPa).*

TABLE 3—*Summary of ASTM C-917 strength data reported to IDOT in 1982.*

Manufacturer	7-Day Compressive Strength, psi[a]				28-Day Compressive Strength, psi[a]			
	Number of Tests	Average	Standard Deviation	CV	Number of Tests	Average	Standard Deviation	CV
No. 2	121	4160	358	8.6	121	5390	373	6.9
No. 3	130	4190	344	8.2	130	5460	462	8.5
No. 4	138	3980	191	4.8	132	4780	234	4.9
No. 5	114	4380	268	6.1	114	5730	301	5.3
No. 6	90	4420	277	6.3	90	5430	345	6.4
No. 7	124	4220	276	6.5	124	5170	280	5.4
No. 8	100	3940	223	5.7	100	5730	267	4.7
No. 9	135	4020	266	6.6	135	5640	261	4.6
No. 10	63	4120	252	6.1	59	5190	242	4.7
No. 11	83	3690	247	6.7	83	4960	367	7.4
No. 13	120	4210	334	7.9	120	5580	434	7.8
No. 15	120	4170	217	5.2	120	5690	287	5.0
No. 17	104	4200	295	7.0	104	5830	411	7.0
No. 20	121	4060	201	5.0	121	5480	311	5.7
No. 22	130	4430	208	4.7	130	5400	252	4.7

[a]1 psi = 0.0069 MPa.

TABLE 4—*Summary of ASTM C-917 strength data reported to IDOT in 1983.*

	7-Day Compressive Strength, psi[a]				28-Day Compressive Strength, psi[a]			
Manufacturer	Number of Tests	Average	Standard Deviation	CV	Number of Tests	Average	Standard Deviation	CV
No. 2	120	4390	352	8.0	120	5620	429	7.6
No. 3	123	4290	254	5.9	123	5700	284	5.0
No. 4	153	3980	203	5.1	152	4860	239	4.9
No. 5	111	4390	286	6.5	111	5720	287	5.0
No. 6	120	4460	202	4.5	120	5490	255	4.6
No. 7	117	4210	239	5.7	117	5410	315	5.8
No. 8	120	4180	283	6.8	120	5710	415	7.3
No. 9	116	3910	227	5.8	116	5740	230	4.0
No. 10	120	4400	222	5.0	120	5410	218	4.0
No. 11	101	3750	209	5.6	101	4950	308	6.2
No. 13	125	4620	283	6.1	125	5870	289	4.9
No. 15	120	4240	170	4.0	120	5670	239	4.2
No. 17	119	4270	334	7.8	119	6090	375	6.2
No. 20	121	4000	177	4.4	113	5280	214	4.1
No. 22	102	4570	167	3.7	102	5522	178	3.2

[a]1 psi = 0.0069 MPa.

TABLE 5—*Summary of ASTM C-917 strength data reported to IDOT in 1984.*

	7-Day Compressive Strength, psi[a]				28-Day Compressive Strength, psi[a]			
Manufacturer	Number of Tests	Average	Standard Deviation	CV	Number of Tests	Average	Standard Deviation	CV
No. 2	120	4310	312	7.2	111	5610	380	6.8
No. 3	121	4070	208	5.1	120	5400	288	5.3
No. 4	156	3910	161	4.1	156	4760	180	3.8
No. 5	115	4400	212	4.8	115	5780	304	5.3
No. 6	120	4420	247	5.6	120	5620	319	5.7
No. 8	120	4090	220	5.4	119	5380	271	5.0
No. 9	119	3990	232	5.8	118	5710	260	4.6
No. 10	120	4230	218	5.2	120	5360	199	3.7
No. 11	116	3880	169	4.4	116	5120	371	7.2
No. 13	121	4420	242	5.5	121	5760	285	4.9
No. 15	120	4180	186	4.4	120	5510	228	4.1
No. 17	117	4460	305	6.8	117	6150	375	6.1
No. 20	120	4000	208	5.2	120	5250	265	5.0
No. 24	112	4120	242	5.9	112	5520	291	5.3

[a]1 psi = 0.0069 MPa.

Test Verification

To verify ASTM C 917 test data reported by each manufacturer, split portions of random samples selected from those tested by the manufacturer in each quarter were also tested by the Department. Results obtained on these samples were compared to determine differences in testing between the two laboratories. Table 14 lists the 7-day strength averages and standard deviations obtained by both the Department and each manufacturer on samples split in the fourth quarter of 1982. Average differences during this period ranged from 54 to 410 psi (0.4 to 2.8 MPa). A statistical paired "t" test, outlined in Appendix X1 of ASTM C 917, was applied to the

TABLE 6—*Seven-day total standard deviation percent of manufacturers reporting less than value listed in Column 1. (Period covered: January thru December 1981.)*

Column 1, psi[a]	1st Quarter	2nd Quarter	3rd Quarter	4th Quarter	Total, Year
450	...	100	...	...	...
400	...	88	...	100	...
350	100	88	...	89	100
300	67	88	...	78	75
250	44	50	100	67	38
200	33	25	57	22	25
150	0	13	14	22	0
100	0	0	0	0	0

[a]1 psi = 0.0069 MPa.

TABLE 7—*Seven-day total standard deviation percent of manufacturers reporting less than value listed in Column 1. (Period covered: January thru December 1982.)*

Column 1, psi[a]	1st Quarter	2nd Quarter	3rd Quarter	4th Quarter	Total, Year
400	...	100	...	...	100
350	...	93	100	...	93
300	100	93	93	100	80
250	92	53	67	67	40
200	50	27	27	33	7
150	17	7	0	13	0
100	0	0	0	0	0

[a]1 psi = 0.0069 MPa.

TABLE 8—*Seven-day total standard deviation percent of manufacturers reporting less than value listed in Column 1. (Period covered: January thru December 1983.)*

Column 1, psi[a]	1st Quarter	2nd Quarter	3rd Quarter	4th Quarter	Total, Year
500	...	100	...	...	...
450	...	93	...	...	...
400	...	93	...	...	100
350	100	93	100	...	93
300	93	87	93	100	87
250	80	73	60	87	60
200	47	47	33	33	20
150	7	7	13	7	0
100	0	0	7	0	0

[a]1 psi = 0.0069 MPa.

results to determine if testing by the manufacturer and the Department was significantly different. A significance level of 0.05 was used. As shown in Table 14, the average difference in eight of the twelve laboratories compared was not significant.

Testing for differences between laboratories is an on-going program. Plant laboratories are required to be inspected by the Bureau of Standards Cement and Concrete Reference Laboratory (CCRL), as is the Department laboratory. If significant differences with a manufacturer

TABLE 9—*Seven-day total standard deviation percent of manufacturers reporting less than value listed in Column 1. (Period covered: January thru December 1984.)*

Column 1, psi[a]	1st Quarter	2nd Quarter	3rd Quarter	4th Quarter	Total, Year
350	100	100	100	. . .	100
300	87	93	94	100	86
250	80	80	88	94	86
200	47	53	53	53	21
150	13	7	18	12	0
100	0	0	0	0	0

[a]1 psi = 0.0069 MPa.

TABLE 10—*Twenty-eight day total standard deviation percent of manufacturers reporting less than value listed in Column 1. (Period covered: January thru December 1981.)*

Column 1, psi[a]	1st Quarter	2nd Quarter	3rd Quarter	4th Quarter	Total, Year
450	100	. . .	. . .	100	. . .
400	89	. . .	. . .	89	100
350	78	100	100	89	75
300	56	88	86	67	63
250	44	63	57	44	25
200	22	38	0	33	25
150	0	13	0	11	0
100	0	0	0	0	0

[a]1 psi = 0.0069 MPa.

TABLE 11—*Twenty-eight day total standard deviation percent of manufacturers reporting less than value listed in Column 1. (Period covered: January thru December 1982.)*

Column 1, psi[a]	1st Quarter	2nd Quarter	3rd Quarter	4th Quarter	Total, Year
500	100	. . .	. . .	. . .	100
450	92	. . .	100	100	93
400	92	100	93	93	80
350	92	93	87	87	67
300	75	60	60	53	47
250	58	27	20	33	13
200	25	7	13	13	0
150	0	0	0	7	0
100	0	0	0	0	0

[a]1 psi = 0.0069 MPa.

TABLE 12—*Twenty-eight day total standard deviation percent of manufacturers reporting less than value listed in Column 1. (Period covered: January thru December 1983.)*

Column 1, psi[a]	1st Quarter	2nd Quarter	3rd Quarter	4th Quarter	Total, Year
450	...	100	100	...	100
400	100	87	93	...	87
350	87	80	87	100	80
300	80	67	80	87	67
250	53	53	33	67	40
200	27	27	20	7	7
150	7	7	0	0	0
100	0	0	0	0	0

[a]1 psi = 0.0069 MPa.

TABLE 13—*Twenty-eight day total standard deviation percent of manufacturers reporting less than value listed in Column 1. (Period covered: January thru December 1984.)*

Column 1, psi[a]	1st Quarter	2nd Quarter	3rd Quarter	4th Quarter	Total, Year
500	100	...	...	...	...
450	93	...	100	100	...
400	93	100	94	88	100
350	87	87	94	88	79
300	67	73	82	88	64
250	53	47	47	71	21
200	27	27	29	24	14
150	0	7	6	12	0
100	0	7	0	0	0
50	0	0	0	0	0

[a]1 psi = 0.0069 MPa.

persist for two or three consecutive quarters, the plant laboratory equipment and methods of test are checked for compliance with the findings of the last CCRL inspection. Results obtained on the CCRL reference samples are also examined. Additional comparison testing may be required to determine the cause for the difference.

Concluding Remarks

The ability of a cement manufacturer to establish a strength level for his product and to maintain a moving average of five within control limits calculated using a given standard deviation of 300 psi (2.1 MPa) is not beyond the capability of the plant quality control. Tables 6 through 9 show that the percentage of manufacturers reporting a 7-day total standard deviation less than 300 psi (2.1 MPa) increased from 75% in 1981, before any uniformity requirement, to 86% in 1984. During this same period, the percent of manufacturers reporting a total standard deviation less than 250 psi (1.7 MPa) increased from 38 to 86%.

Figure 3 shows graphically the result of the Department's strength uniformity requirement on the variability of one manufacturer's shipments. The moving averages of five for the 7- and 28-day C 917 strength data are plotted for manufacturer No. 3 for the years 1982, 1983, and 1984. The 7-day total standard deviation for shipments from this plant was reduced from 344 psi (2.4 MPa) in 1982 to 208 psi (1.4 MPa) in 1984.

TABLE 14—Comparison of 7-day strength results on split samples, psi[a].

| Manufacturer | Number of Tests | IDOT | | Manufacturer | | Average Difference | Standard Deviation of Difference | Significant Difference |
		Average	Standard Deviation	Average	Standard Deviation			
No. 2	11	4338	202	4427	305	89	266	No
No. 4	11	4084	348	4004	159	80	226	No
No. 5	10	4163	263	4314	322	151	277	No
No. 6	11	4396	248	4480	230	84	258	No
No. 7	10	4047	319	4261	224	214	217	Yes
No. 8	11	3626	185	3960	291	334	258	Yes
No. 9	10	4025	284	4079	184	54	242	No
No. 10	10	4146	201	4211	197	65	139	No
No. 11	11	3827	298	3671	224	156	341	No
No. 13	12	4152	184	4562	157	410	184	Yes
No. 17	11	3904	343	4046	244	142	252	No
No. 20	11	3661	176	4049	117	388	109	Yes

[a]1 psi = 0.0069 MPa.

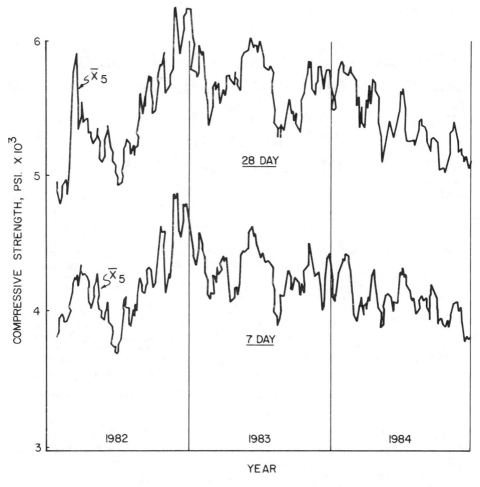

FIG. 3—*Plot of moving averages of five for C 109 mortar cube strengths as reported by Manufacturer No. 3 for the period 1982-1984 (1 psi = 0.0069 MPa).*

Other manufacturers have experienced little difficulty in meeting the Department's uniformity requirement. In 1984, the first complete year of operating under the final version of the Department's strength requirement, only two manufacturers exceeded the control limits momentarily before corrective action was taken to bring the moving average back within the limits.

The Department realizes that changes in plant equipment or raw materials can affect the uniformity of the product and encourage manufacturers to anticipate when these changes may occur and keep the Department apprised of these events.

Good communications and accurate test data are necessary to improve long-term quality control—a goal of equal importance to the cement manufacturer and the Illinois Department of Transportation.

Toy S. Poole[1]

Summary of Statistical Analyses of Specification Mortar Cube Test Results from Various Cement Suppliers, Including Four Types of Cement Approved for Corps of Engineers Projects

REFERENCE: Poole, Toy A., **"Summary of Statistical Analyses of Specification Mortar Cube Test Results from Various Cement Suppliers, Including Four Types of Cement Approved for Corps of Engineers Projects,"** *Uniformity of Cement Strength, STP 961,* E. Farkas and P. Klieger, Eds., American Society for Testing and Materials, Philadelphia, 1987, pp. 14–21.

ABSTRACT: Within-plant variation in compressive strength was examined for 95 portland cement sources. Levels of variation were found to vary with test age and type of cement. Standard deviations generally increased with age and were generally higher in Type III and Type V cements. The effect of type of sampling on estimates of within-plant standard deviation in compressive strength was examined. Test samples represented by 24-h production composites exhibited measurably less variation than the same cements when represented by grab samples.

KEY WORDS: within-plant variation, standard deviation, compressive strength, composite samples, grab samples

The purposes of this report are: (1) to quantitatively describe variation in compressive strength in a wide variety of cements based on the manufacturer's own quality control data, and (2) to compare the effect of type of sampling on measured variability from a single source, using both the manufacturer's data and data generated at our own laboratory.

The Corps of Engineers has developed the Cement Quality Management System (CQMS) as a way to obtain some estimate of expected performance of cements based on manufacturers' test reports and possibly to obviate the system of sampling and sealing individual lots of cement. Every six months manufacturers participating in the CQMS program submit their most recent quality control data for an analysis of within-plant variability. In the process of collecting such data, the Cement and Pozzolan Unit at the Waterways Experiment Station (WES) has assembled information on strength development and variation in strength development for a large number of cements marketed in the United States. Enough information is on file to examine patterns of variation among types of cement and test ages. This information is also potentially useful in evaluating the uniformity of cement from a single source as described in ASTM C 917 [Method for Evaluation of Cement Strength Uniformity from a Single Source (C 917-82)].

Use of manufacturers' quality control data to estimate uniformity in the context of ASTM C 917 could create a problem because manufacturers' test reports are usually based on composite

[1]Chemist, Waterways Experiment Station, Corps of Engineers, Department of the Army, Vicksburg, MS 39180.

14

samples of 24 h of production. Composite sampling has the effect of smoothing strength variations when compared to data generated from point samples (grab samples). ASTM C 917 specifies that data should be taken as grab samples. Periodic testing at WES of samples taken at construction projects to supplement manufacturers' data are based on grab samples; consequently, they provide a means of evaluating the magnitude of the effect of the type of sampling on measures of variability.

Procedure

Data

Manufacturers' data representing 95 sources of portland cements are currently on file at WES as part of the CQMS. These are distributed among four types [as described in ASTM Specification for Portland Cement (C 150-85a)] and specified for purchase as follows: 20 Type I, 46 Type II, 9 Type I/II (meets both Type I and Type II specifications), 8 Type III, and 12 Type V cements. Each cement is represented by 40 test reports, covering from 30 days to one year of production, depending on the manufacturer. These analyses are based on compressive strength determinations of 2-in. mortar cubes, tested according to ASTM C 109 [Standard Method for Compressive Strength of Hydraulic Cement Mortars (Using 2-in. or 50-mm Cube Specimens) (C 109-86)].

Repeated sampling and testing of cements from more than 75 sources has been performed at WES, but only a small number of these represent extensive enough sampling to provide a valid estimate of the variation in compressive strength of grab-sampled cements for comparison with the manufacturers' composite sampled data. Nine Type II cements, for which CQMS data also exist, were sampled extensively enough to make useful comparisons.

Data Analysis

For purposes of describing within-plant variation, CQMS data derived from each manufacturer's reports were compiled to obtain the following information: (1) mean strength, standard deviation, and coefficient of variation were calculated ($N = 40$) for each reported age (3, 7, and 28 days specified for Types I, II, I/II, and V cements, or 1 and 3 days specified for Type III cements); (2) these data were then pooled for each cement type and analyzed for patterns of strength development and patterns of variation among types and test ages; (3) the statistical significance of differences in strength, standard deviation, and coefficient of variation among types was analyzed in a one-way analysis of variance (ANOVA) at each reported age. Where the ANOVA indicated that significant differences existed among means, then Duncan's New Multiple Range Test was used to determine specifically which means were responsible for that result. Age-dependent patterns were analyzed by Pearson's correlation coefficient. A Type I error of less than or equal to 5% was taken as an indication of statistical significance in all comparisons.

For purposes of comparing variation among grab samples calculated from WES data with variation among composite samples calculated from manufacturer's CQMS data, these two sources of data need to be put on a similar basis. The procedure described in following paragraphs represents an effort to accomplish this. Our WES data for the nine selected cements were examined by analysis of variance to determine if cements were more variable between years than within years. The purpose of this analysis was to determine whether data could be combined over many years of sampling without introducing year-to-year changes as another source of variation. Variation among years was significant, therefore standard deviation values were calculated for each year of reporting and averaged over all years in which that cement was tested. This mean value was weighted for the number of tests performed in each year. The standard deviation within each of the nine cements represented in the WES data was then compared with the standard deviation calculated from the CQMS data, based on manufacturers' reports, for the same cement over a one-year period. The statistical significance of these comparisons was evaluated by Student's t-Test for paired observations.

Results and Discussion

Variation Among Sources

Data representing compressive strengths and within-plant variation in compressive strength for each type of cement from manufacturers' CQMS data are summarized in Table 1.

Strength development curves for CQMS cements are illustrated in Fig. 1. As expected, Type III cement showed the most rapid strength development, although 28-day data were insufficient ($N = 1$) to be conclusive. Type I and I/II cements were not statistically different at any test age. Both of these showed significantly higher strengths through 7 days than the Type II and V cements. Strengths of Type II and V cements were not statistically different at any test age. Strengths of all cements tended to converge at the 28-day test age, with differences not being statistically significant.

The mean and range of within-plant standard deviations in compressive strengths were similar to the values reported in Appendix X2 of ASTM C 917 (only 7- and 28-day data are reported). There was some pattern to this variation, as described in following paragraphs.

In general, standard deviations in compressive strength were found to increase with test age (Fig. 2). This is expected since the cements are gaining strength during this time and measurement of higher strengths often is accompanied by a higher standard deviation. However, relative uniformity tends to improve with age, as indicated by a decrease in mean coefficients of variation (standard deviation $\times$ 100/strength) with test age (Fig. 3). The reason for this increase in relative uniformity is not apparent.

Standard deviations also varied with the type of cement. However, cement types did not segregate as neatly in this property as they did in the strength properties just described. Rather, mean standard deviations tended to exhibit gradients among cement types at each test age, with considerable overlap among individual sources. These relationships are illustrated in Figs. 4, 5, and 6. Type III cements were consistently the most variable, although 28-day variation was represented by data from only one source and consequently not conclusive. Type V and II cements were next most variable, in that order, followed by Type I and I/II cements. The relative ranking of the latter two types changed with test age, but the difference was never statistically significant. This gradient among types was statistically significant at 3- and 7-day test ages, but not statistically significant at the 28-day test age, although the relative ranking was essentially unchanged.

Analysis of coefficient of variations among cement types generally supported the same patterns observed in the analysis of standard deviation patterns.

In general, it appeared that the higher levels of variation were associated with cements commonly not produced on a daily basis, but rather produced on an intermittent basis. It is plausible that the adjustment of manufacturing parameters required to shift production to specialty cements would result in a less uniform product.

Effect of Type of Sampling on Standard Deviation

On the average, analyses of grab samples resulted in higher standard deviations than analyses of the same sources of cements sampled as 24-h composites. For 3-day tests, the grab-sampled test results averaged 63 psi higher than the composite-sampled test results. At 7 days the aver-

TABLE 1—*Summary of within-plant C 109 compressive strength data derived from WES CQMS records.*

Type I Cements	Age = 3 Days	Age = 7 Days	Age = 28 Days
No. of plants	20	20	20
Mean strength, psi	3460	4583	5987
Mean within-plant std. dev.	212	234	282
Minimum value	71	126	170
Maximum value	394	418	407
Mean within-plant C.V., %	6.12	5.10	4.68

Type I-II Cements	Age = 3 Days	Age = 7 Days	Age = 28 Days
No. of plants	9	9	7
Mean strength, psi	3260	4342	6040
Mean within-plant std. dev.	201	233	321
Minimum value	52	70	240
Maximum value	385	333	458
Mean within-plant C.V., %	6.22	5.39	5.30

Type II Cements	Age = 3 Days	Age = 7 Days	Age = 28 Days
No. of plants	46	46	39
Mean strength, psi	2688	3658	5466
Mean within-plant std. dev.	236	301	360
Minimum value	73	118	100
Maximum value	457	498	826
Mean within-plant C.V., %	9.19	8.55	6.65

Type III Cements	Age = 1 Day	Age = 3 Days	Age = 28 Days
No. of plants	8	8	1
Mean strength, psi	3161	4855	6240
Mean within-plant std. dev.	272	301	...
Minimum value	166	230	449
Maximum value	326	344	449
Mean within-plant C.V., %	8.60	6.25	7.19

Type V Cements	Age = 3 Days	Age = 7 Days	Age = 28 Days
No. of plants	12	12	12
Mean strength, psi	2654	3661	5507
Mean within-plant std. dev.	287	344	375
Minimum value	176	219	269
Maximum value	485	478	468
Mean within-plant C.V., %	10.85	9.44	6.85

NOTE: MPa = 0.006895 × psi.

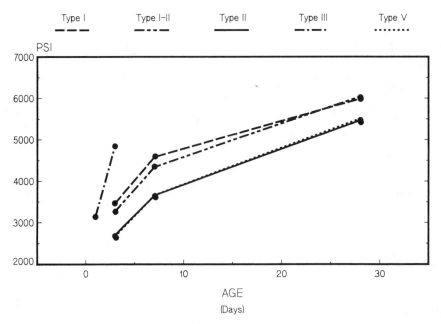

FIG. 1—*Compressive strength of C 109 cubes versus age, by cement types (MPa = 0.006895 × psi).*

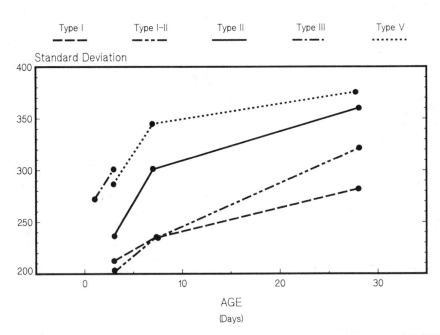

FIG. 2—*Mean within-plant standard deviation (psi) versus age, by cement types (MPa = 0.006895 × psi).*

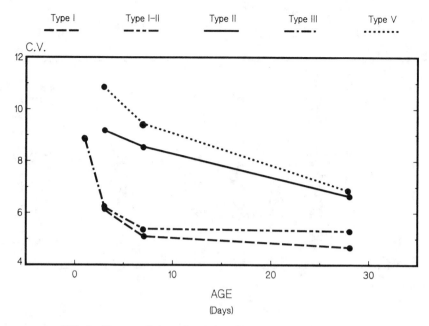

FIG. 3—*Mean coefficient of variation (%) versus age, by cement types.*

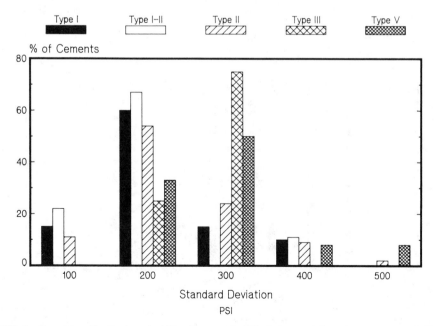

FIG. 4—*Frequency distribution of within-plant standard deviations at 3 days, by cement type (MPa = 0.006895 × psi). Data are expressed as the percent of the total number of sources represented by each type.*

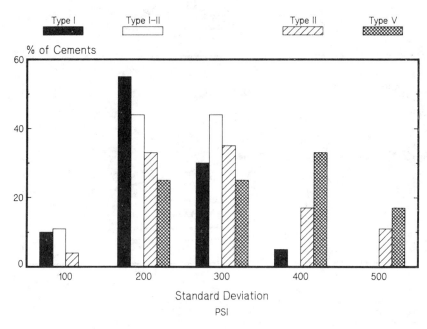

FIG. 5—*Frequency distribution of within-plant standard deviations at 7 days, by cement type (MPa =
0.006895 × psi). Data are expressed as the percent of the total number of sources represented by each type.*

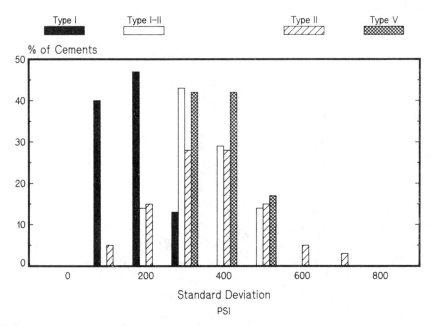

FIG. 6—*Frequency distribution of within-plant standard deviations at 28 days, by cement type (MPa =
0.006895 × psi). Data are expressed as the percent of the total number of sources represented by each type.*

TABLE 2—*Comparison of standard deviations in compressive strength between grab-sampled cements (WES Data) and composite-sampled cements (CQMS data).*

AGE = 3 DAYS

Plant	Years Sampled	Standard Deviation, psi, WES	Standard Deviation, psi, CQMS	Difference
1	9	263	209	54
2	4	259	241	18
3	6	342	278	64
4	8	317	375	−58
5	9	291	194	97
6	4	207	208	−1
7	6	340	204	136
8	6	322	221	101
9	7	307	151	156

NOTE: mean difference = 63 psi; t = 2.76; P < 0.05; 8 d.f.; MPa = 0.006895 × psi.

AGE = 7 DAYS

Plant	Years Sampled	Standard Deviation, psi, WES	Standard Deviation, psi, CQMS	Difference
1	9	286	186	100
2	4	260	288	−28
3	6	336	307	29
4	8	420	355	65
5	9	392	292	100
6	4	231	215	16
7	6	432	359	73
8	6	410	247	163
9	7	383	180	203

NOTE: mean difference = 80 psi; t = 3.33; P < 0.02; 8 d.f.; MPa = 0.006895 × psi.

age difference was 80 psi. Both of these differences were statistically significant and represent about a 28% increase in the measured standard deviation. These data are summarized in Table 2.

This result could be due to excessive variation in WES sampling and testing. However, this does not appear to be the case, since our within-laboratory coefficient of variation during this time was 2.7%. This is within the scope of the 3.8% coefficient of variation cited in ASTM C 109 as normal within laboratory variation.

This result indicates that type of sampling is a factor which should be considered in evaluating uniformity data from a single source. In general, quality control data representing composite sampling cannot be used directly for uniformity comparisons made in the context of ASTM C 917 without there being some bias in the analysis.

Hassan A. Al-Badr[1] and A. D. Kilpadikar[1]

Uniformity in Compressive Strengths of Cement and Corresponding Concrete

REFERENCE: Al-Badr, H. A. and Kilpadikar, A. D., **"Uniformity in Compressive Strengths of Cement and Corresponding Concrete,"** *Uniformity of Cement Strength, ASTM STP 961,* E. Farkas and P. Klieger, Eds., American Society for Testing and Materials, Philadelphia, 1987, pp. 22–29.

ABSTRACT: This article shows how ASTM Method for Evaluation of Cement Strength Uniformity from a Single Source (C 917-82) serves as a valuable tool in ascertaining the uniformity in the quality of cement produced. The results obtained on compressive strength tests of both cement and concrete—the cement being tested at Saudi Kuwaiti Cement Manufacturing Co. (SKC manufacturing quality control laboratory) and the concrete (using SKC cement) at the quality control laboratory of Saudi Arabian Vulcan Limited, a ready mix concrete plant—clearly indicate that there is very good uniformity in quality of cement produced at SKC's factory situated at Khursaniyah (in the Eastern Province of Saudi Arabia) with a capacity of 7000 MT/day of cement clinker due to the level of automation adopted in process control. Thus the article brings out that, in modern cement plants which are usually large in capacity, C 917-82 is a suitable yardstick to assess whether the quality control procedures exercised are effective.

KEY WORDS: cement, cement product (concrete), compressive strength, mode, uniformity, evaluation

Modern cement plants have high-rated capacities, and Saudi Kuwaiti Cement Manufacturing Co. has a production capacity of 7000 MT/day of cement clinker. As such the yardstick of measuring the quality of cement produced should be stringent.

Automation, and even more so X-ray fluorescence interfaced with a computer to monitor the process, has revolutionized the concept of quality control and has raised it to a level close to perfection. Thus, quality control is not only a byword, but built into the product and not merely inspection of the product produced.

ASTM Method for Evaluation of Cement Strength Uniformity from a Single Source (C 917-82) serves as a useful standard for self-analysis. For Saudi Kuwaiti Cement Manufacturing Co. (SKC), use of this specification has not only helped, but also served as a valuable tool for assessing the quality of cement produced.

It should not be enough to rest on one's laurels and say that good cement is being produced, but rather to take a step forward and ascertain from clients who use the cement whether they are satisfied. Thus, a rapport was established with one of the ready mix concrete clients, Saudi Arabian Vulcan Ltd. (SAVL), Jubail, who are using bulk cement on a regular basis from SKC.

Data Presentation

Cement Testing

Compressive strength tests on cement mortar were carried out in the SKC quality control laboratory and tested in accordance with Test Method for Compressive Strength of Hydraulic

---

[1]General manager, and manager—Process and Quality Control, respectively, Saudi Kuwaiti Cement Manufacturing Co., Saudi Arabia.

Cement Mortars (Using 2-in. or 50-mm Cube Specimens) (C 109-86). Grab samples were drawn from each of the bulk trucks, and test samples of a minimum of 5 kg were prepared as specified in Paragraph 5 of C 917. These tests samples are average samples representing daily dispatches, varying from 2 to 5 bulkers, that are sent to SAVL, representing 80 to 200 MT of bulk cement (Type V).

The entire test covers a period of about two months, from 15 June 1985 to 15 Aug. 1985. Data are presented in Table 1, Column 1 indicating the date of samples drawn and representing the average (shipping/dispatches) of the particular day.

Column 2 exhibits the sample designation, being split up into sample number and followed by a suffix "a" or "b." Series "a" signifies the initial test to arrive at the total standard deviation, that is, "St." Series "b" indicates the results obtained in duplicate testing on different days on one each out of every three samples in series, as indicated in Clause 6.2.1, to obtain the standard deviation (Se) for testing.

The various calculated values are summarized in Table 2. Figures 1 and 2 depict the graphic representation of compressive strengths at ages 7 and 28 days, respectively, for the different samples under study.

Concrete Testing

SAVL has submitted compressive strength results on samples collected by them during the period 15 June 1986 to 31 July 1986. The tests represent 6 m³ concrete batches mixed in a central batching plant and supplied to the local market. Concrete is designed for a 100-mm slump, with

TABLE 1—*Compressive strength on cement mortar, Kg/cm² (psi).*

Date Shipped	Sample Number	7 Day		28 Day	
		Sample	Average 5	Sample	Average 5
15.06.85	1a	338.1 (4801)	. . . . . .	419.8 (5961)	. . . . . .
	1b	335.0 (4757)	. . . . . .	423.2 (6010)	. . . . . .
16.06.85	2a	326.8 (4641)	. . . . . .	414.7 (5889)	. . . . . .
17.06.85	3a	334.0 (4743)	. . . . . .	422.3 (5996)	. . . . . .
22.06.85	4a	329.9 (4685)	. . . . . .	402.5 (5715)	. . . . . .
	4b	318.7 (4525)	. . . . . .	389.1 (5525)	. . . . . .
23.06.85	5a	326.8 (4641)	331.1 (4702)	420.4 (5970)	415.9 (5906)
24.06.85	6a	317.7 (4511)	327.0 (4644)	397.3 (5642)	411.4 (5842)
25.06.85	7a	319.7 (4540)	325.6 (4624)	401.4 (5700)	408.8 (5805)
	7b	305.4 (4337)	324.4 (4606)	390.2 (5541)	407.5 (5787)
26.06.85	8a	327.9 (4656)	324.0 (4606)	415.7 (5903)	407.5 (5787)
27.06.85	9a	327.9 (4656)	324.0 (4601)	417.7 (5932)	410.6 (5831)
29.06.85	10a	315.6 (4482)	321.8 (4569)	404.5 (5744)	407.3 (5784)
	10b	307.5 (4366)	. . . . . .	393.2 (5584)	. . . . . .
31.06.85	11a	324.8 (4612)	323.2 (4589)	411.6 (5845)	410.2 (5825)
01.07.85	12a	332.0 (4714)	325.6 (4624)	418.8 (5947)	413.7 (5874)
02.07.85	13a	339.1 (4815)	327.9 (4656)	420.8 (5976)	414.7 (5889)
	13b	322.7 (4583)	. . . . . .	407.5 (5787)	. . . . . .
03.07.85	14a	325.8 (4627)	327.5 (4650)	413.7 (5874)	413.9 (5877)
04.07.85	15a	305.4 (4337)	325.4 (4621)	392.3 (5570)	411.4 (5842)
06.07.85	16a	311.5 (4424)	322.7 (4583)	395.3 (5613)	408.1 (5796)
	16b	299.3 (4250)	. . . . . .	384.1 (5454)	. . . . . .
07.07.85	17a	318.7 (4525)	320.1 (4546)	410.6 (5831)	406.5 (5773)
08.07.85	18a	315.6 (4482)	315.4 (4479)	405.5 (5758)	403.5 (5729)
09.07.85	19a	329.9 (4685)	316.0 (4490)	413.7 (5874)	403.5 (5729)
	19b	312.5 (4438)	. . . . . .	406.5 (5773)	. . . . . .

TABLE 1—*Continued.*

Date Shipped	Sample Number	7 Day		28 Day	
		Sample	Average 5	Sample	Average 5
10.07.85	20a	316.6 (4496)	318.5 (4522)	406.5 (5773)	406.3 (5770)
11.07.85	21a	300.3 (4264)	317.0 (4490)	394.3 (5599)	406.1 (5767)
13.07.85	22a	309.5 (4395)	314.3 (4464)	404.5 (5744)	404.9 (5749)
	22b	307.5 (4366)	... ...	389.9 (5537)	... ...
14.07.85	23a	304.4 (4322)	312.1 (4432)	393.2 (5584)	402.5 (5715)
15.07.85	24a	327.9 (4656)	311.8 (4427)	418.7 (5945)	403.5 (5729)
16.07.85	25a	334.0 (4743)	315.2 (4476)	413.7 (5874)	404.9 (5749)
	25b	310.5 (4409)	... ...	404.5 (5744)	... ...
17.07.85	26a	318.7 (4525)	318.9 (4528)	407.5 (5787)	407.5 (5787)
20.07.85	27a	332.0 (4714)	323.4 (4592)	411.6 (5845)	408.9 (5807)
21.07.85	28a	312.5 (4438)	325.0 (4615)	405.5 (5758)	411.4 (5842)
	28b	316.6 (4496)	... ...	394.3 (5599)	... ...
23.07.85	29a	332.0 (4714)	325.8 (4627)	414.7 (5889)	410.6 (5831)
24.07.85	30a	325.8 (4627)	324.2 (4604)	406.5 (5773)	409.2 (5810)
25.07.85	31a	347.3 (4931)	329.9 (4685)	429.0 (6092)	413.5 (5871)
	31b	335.0 (4757)	... ...	412.7 (5860)	... ...
27.07.85	32a	302.3 (4293)	324.0 (4601)	395.3 (5613)	410.2 (5825)
28.07.85	33a	319.7 (4540)	325.4 (4621)	398.4 (5657)	408.8 (5805)
29.07.85	34a	311.5 (4424)	321.3 (4563)	390.1 (5540)	403.9 (5735)
31.07.85	35a	303.4 (4308)	316.9 (4499)	390.2 (5541)	400.6 (5688)
01.08.85	36a	315.4 (4479)	310.5 (4409)	414.9 (5892)	397.8 (5649)
03.08.85	37a	328.7 (4667)	315.7 (4483)	423.1 (6008)	403.4 (5728)
	37b	329.7 (4682)	... ...	406.8 (5776)	... ...
04.08.85	38a	317.5 (4508)	315.3 (4477)	409.9 (5820)	405.6 (5760)
06.08.85	39a	330.7 (4696)	319.1 (4531)	422.1 (5994)	412.1 (5851)
07.08.85	40a	318.5 (4522)	322.1 (4574)	399.6 (5674)	413.9 (5878)
	40b	321.5 (4566)	... ...	393.5 (5587)	... ...
08.08.85	41a	314.4 (4464)	321.9 (4571)	409.9 (5820)	412.9 (5863)
10.08.85	42a	324.6 (4609)	321.1 (4560)	417.0 (5921)	411.7 (5846)
11.08.85	43a	313.4 (4450)	320.3 (4548)	394.4 (5600)	408.6 (5802)
	43b	304.2 (4319)	... ...	390.8 (5550)	... ...
12.08.85	44a	316.4 (4493)	317.5 (4508)	395.5 (5616)	403.3 (5727)
13.08.85	45a	319.5 (4537)	317.7 (4511)	403.7 (5733)	404.9 (5738)
14.08.85	46a	328.7 (4667)	320.5 (4551)	410.8 (5834)	404.3 (5741)
	46b	323.6 (4595)	... ...	403.7 (5733)	... ...
17.08.85	47a	337.9 (4798)	323.2 (4589)	416.0 (5907)	404.1 (5738)
18.08.85	48a	312.3 (4435)	323.0 (4586)	404.7 (5747)	406.1 (5767)
19.08.85	49a	322.5 (4580)	324.2 (4603)	408.8 (5805)	408.8 (5805)
	49b	312.3 (4435)	... ...	407.7 (5789)	... ...
21.08.85	50a	343.0 (4870)	328.9 (4670)	417.0 (5921)	411.5 (5843)
22.08.85	51a	315.4 (4479)	327.0 (4632)	407.8 (5791)	410.8 (5834)
24.08.85	52a	321.5 (4566)	323.0 (4586)	395.4 (5615)	406.8 (5776)
	52b	323.6 (4595)	... ...	399.4 (5671)	... ...
31.08.85	53a	315.4 (4479)	323.6 (4595)	422.0 (5993)	410.2 (5825)
01.09.85	54a	309.3 (4392)	321.0 (4557)	393.7 (5590)	407.2 (5782)
02.09.85	55a	332.7 (4725)	318.9 (4528)	411.3 (5841)	406.1 (5766)
	55b	314.4 (4464)	... ...	398.9 (5665)	... ...
03.09.85	56a	324.6 (4609)	320.7 (4554)	405.4 (5756)	405.6 (5759)
04.09.85	57a	319.5 (4537)	320.3 (4548)	406.3 (5770)	407.7 (5790)
05.09.85	58a	326.6 (4638)	322.5 (4580)	420.6 (5973)	407.4 (5786)
	58b	328.7 (4667)	... ...	422.7 (6003)	... ...
07.09.85	59a	318.5 (4522)	324.4 (4606)	388.4 (5515)	406.4 (5771)
08.09.85	60a	320.5 (4551)	322.0 (4572)	410.3 (5826)	407.0 (5768)

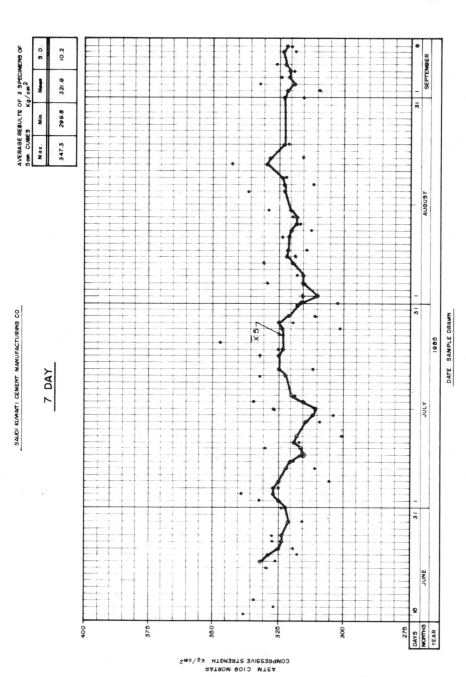

FIG. 1—*Seven-day compressive strength on daily cement dispatches to SAVL over a period of about three months.*

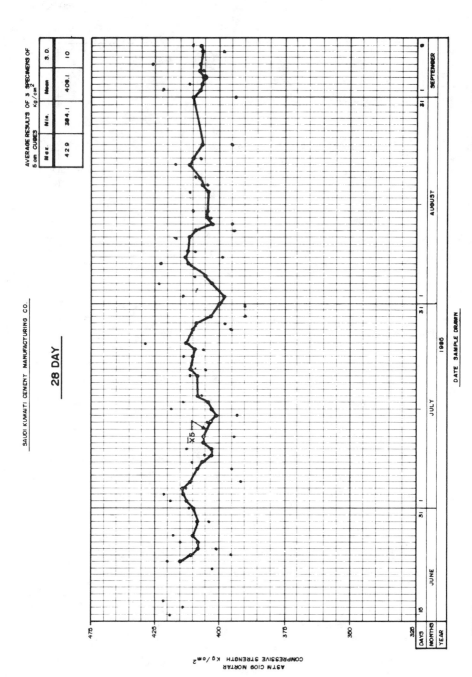

FIG. 2—*Twenty-eight-day compressive strength on daily cement dispatches to SAVL over a period of about three months.*

TABLE 2—*Sample uniformity test report, SKC bulk loading (Type V) (from 15 June 85 to 8 Sept. 85).*

Item	7 Day	28 Day
Average strength, Kg/cm² (psi)	321.9 (4571)	408.1 (5795)
Total standard deviation, Kg/cm² (psi)	10.2 (145)	10.0 (142)
Number tests, deviation	60	60
Testing standard deviation (Se), Kg/cm² (psi)	10.1 (144)	8.1 (115)
Number tests, deviation	20	20
Corrected standard deviation (Sc), Kg/cm² (psi)	6.3 (9.0)	5.8 (83)

no intentional entrainment of air; a water-reducing admixture "Conplast 211" was used for Type V Saudi Kuwaiti cement. The concrete specimens tested for compressive strengths were cylinders of 150 by 300 mm.

During the past six years Saudi Arabian Vulcan Limited has produced in Saudi Arabia over 3 million m³ of high quality concrete. The concrete, in strength classes of 211.3 kg/cm² (3000 psi) and 281.7 kg/cm² (4000 psi), has consistently complied with the specification standards of the design engineers and the American Concrete Institute (ACI) 318 Building Code. The coarse aggregate for this concrete has been crushed stone from the Abu Hadriyah quarries operated by SAVL. The sands were selected from dunes meeting the established fineness modulus and cleanliness requirements. Results are tabulated in Tables 3 and 4 and a graph is represented by Fig. 3.

TABLE 3—*Compressive strength, kg/cm² (concrete tested by SAVL, Jubail, Saudi Arabia).*

Sample Number	7 Day		28 Day	
	Sample	Average 5	Sample	Average 5
1	283.8	...	326.8	...
2	275.4	...	304.9	...
3	288.7	...	314.8	...
4	278.9	...	334.5	...
5	269.0	279.2	339.4	324.1
6	283.8	279.2	332.4	325.2
7	298.6	283.8	331.0	330.4
8	288.0	283.7	317.6	331.0
9	261.0	280.1	331.0	330.3
10	288.7	284.1	330.3	328.5
11	271.8	281.7	299.3	319.7
12	266.2	275.2	333.1	322.3
13	288.7	275.4	344.4	327.6
14	254.2	273.9	298.6	321.1
15	252.8	266.8	302.8	315.6
16	276.8	267.7	347.9	325.4
17	256.3	265.8	309.9	320.7
18	278.9	263.8	326.8	317.2
19	259.2	264.8	298.6	317.2
20	264.1	267.0	314.1	319.4
21	291.5	270.7	332.4	316.3
22	264.1	271.5	316.2	317.6
23	240.1	263.8	299.3	312.1
24	288.0	269.6	332.4	318.9
25	249.3	266.6	326.8	321.4

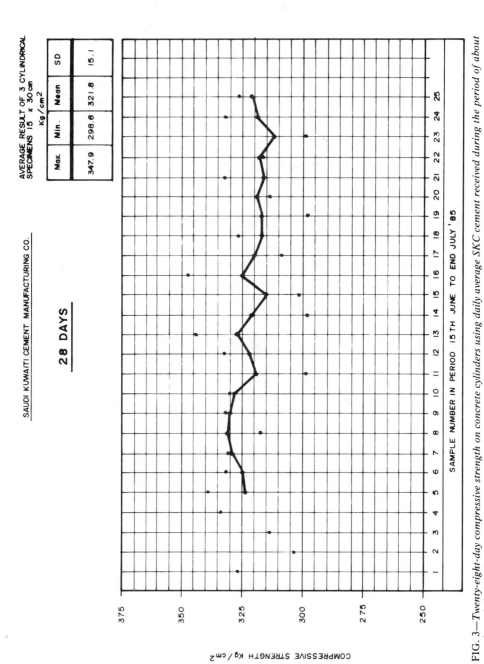

FIG. 3—Twenty-eight-day compressive strength on concrete cylinders using daily average SKC cement received during the period of about one-and-one-half months.

TABLE 4—*Summary of test results, Al Khafji plant (tested by SAVL, Jubail, Saudi Arabia), cement type: V, cement content: 325 kg/m³.*

Item	7 Day	28 Day
Average strength, Kg/cm² (psi)	272.7 (3873)	321.8 (4570)
Standard deviation, Kg/cm² (psi)	15.5 (219.7)	15.1 (214.5)
Number of sample	25	25

NOTE: Minimum 28 days strength required, Kg/cm² = 281.7; minimum required cement = 300 Kg/m³; mix design (kg/m³).

Cement	Sand, SSD	Coarse Aggregate, SSD	Water
325	720	1090	184

NOTE: Coarse aggregate used: crushed limestone (Abu Hadriyah); bulk specific gravity (SSD) [ASTM Test Method for Specific Gravity and Absorption of Coarse Aggregate (C 127-84)] = 2.6; absorption, % (ASTM C 127) = 1.0 to 1.5; Los Angeles abrasion, % [ASTM Test Method for Resistance to Degradation of Small-Size Coarse Aggregate by Abrasion and Impact in the Los Angeles Machine (C 131-81)] = 25 to 35.

Interpretation of Results

Table 2 clearly shows that the corrected standard deviations (Sc) at 7 and 28 days are 6.3 kg/cm² (90 psi) and 5.8 kg/cm² (85 psi), respectively. These results indicate that there is good uniformity in the quality of cement produced with respect to the property under study, that is, compressive strength. Figures 1 and 2 also exhibit the uniform trend.

Table 3 clearly shows that the strengths of concrete are markedly uniform and are strikingly apparent as brought out in Table 4, as the standard deviations at 7 and 28 days are 15.5 kg/cm² (219.7 psi) and 15.1 kg/cm² (214.5 psi), respectively.

The uniformity in compression strengths of cement mortar and concrete shows comparable or equivalent values, as both tests were carried out in almost the same period, namely, mid-June to August, on separate samples drawn from bulk trucks at the two investigating locations.

The graphic representation of 28-day compressive strength of concrete against time as shown in Fig. 3 clearly brings out the narrow variation in the compressive strengths.

Conclusion

Compressive strength tests on cement as per ASTM C 917-82 carried out by SKC in our own quality control laboratory show a very good uniformity in quality. Also, this has special significance as these results are reconfirmed by the findings of the concrete quality control laboratory of SAVL on ready mix concrete produced by them using SKC cement.

James H. Pielert[1] and Curtis B. Spring[2]

Application of CCRL Data in the Development of Cement Standards

REFERENCE: Pielert, J. H. and Spring, C. B., **"Application of CCRL Data in the Development of Cement Standards,"** *Uniformity of Cement Strength, ASTM STP 961,* E. Farkas and P. Klieger, Eds., American Society for Testing and Materials, Philadelphia, 1987, pp. 30-41.

ABSTRACT: The Cement and Concrete Reference Laboratory (CCRL) through its Laboratory inspection and proficiency sample programs collects data which are useful in the development of cement and concrete standards. This paper outlines the scope of CCRL activities, discusses specific examples of technical studies which support standard development, and outlines areas of potential CCRL support to standards committees. CCRL inspections are conducted in laboratories equipped to perform tests on cement, concrete, concrete aggregate, and steel reinforcing bars. The program for the distribution of proficiency samples includes portland cement, portland cement concrete, blended cement, and masonry cement. Data from these programs have over the years been made available to the appropriate ASTM committees. CCRL also studies technical problems of interest to ASTM Committee C-1 on Cement and Committee C-9 on Concrete and Concrete Aggregates. Several activities are presented to illustrate the application of CCRL data.

KEY WORDS: buildings, cement, concrete, construction, quality assurance, standards, structures

The Construction Materials Reference Laboratories (CMRL) is part of the Building Materials Division of the Center for Building Technology at the National Bureau of Standards (NBS). The CMRL consists of the Cement and Concrete Reference Laboratory (CCRL), sponsored by ASTM, and the AASHTO Materials Reference Laboratory (AMRL), sponsored by the American Association of State Highway and Transportation Officials (AASHTO). The goal of the CMRL is to promote improvement in the quality of testing of construction materials in the nation's testing laboratories. This is accomplished through assessing and developing test methods, participating in the formulation of national standards, and providing support to quality assurance programs [1,2].

The purpose of the present paper is to describe the CCRL programs, point out the nature and potential uses of its data bases, provide examples of technical studies, and identify specific CCRL activities which may provide technical support to ASTM committees concerned with cement, concrete, and concrete aggregates.

Background

In the early part of the 20th century, various technical organizations, including NBS, the U.S. Army Corps of Engineers, the American Society of Civil Engineers, ASTM Committee C-1 on Cement, and the Portland Cement Association, began efforts to improve and standardize the

[1]Group leader, Construction Materials Reference Laboratories, National Bureau of Standards, Gaithersburg, MD 20899.
[2]Senior laboratory technologist, Cement and Concrete Reference Laboratory, National Bureau of Standards, Gaithersburg, MD 20899.

specifications and methods for testing portland cement [3,4]. This eventually led to the establishment of the Cement Reference Laboratory (CRL) in April, 1929 at NBS with ASTM Committee C-1 as its sponsor. Inspection of laboratories, which includes an assessment of test equipment and procedures, was designated as the primary CRL activity. Until 1947 the inspections were limited to laboratories performing physical tests on hydraulic cements. Subsequently, the activity was gradually expanded to include concrete testing. ASTM Committee C-9 on Concrete and Concrete Aggregates became a joint sponsor in 1958, and the expanded service, including both cement and concrete, was made available to all laboratories. The name Cement and Concrete Reference Laboratory (CCRL) was adopted in 1960.

The CCRL has four major functions directed toward an improvement in the quality of testing materials used in construction based on ASTM standards: (1) inspecting laboratories that test cement, concrete, concrete aggregates, and reinforcing steel; (2) conducting proficiency test sample programs for portland cement, blended cement, masonry cement, and portland cement concrete; (3) participating in the work of technical committees such as those of ASTM and ACI; and (4) studying problems related to the testing of construction materials included in the CCRL programs. The first two of these are considered the primary functions and are supported by fees paid by the participants.

Nature and Use of the Existing CCRL Data Bases

Overview of the Laboratory Inspection Program

Inspection of testing laboratories is considered the most important CCRL activity. Use of the service is on a voluntary basis and an inspection visit is scheduled only after a request has been received from a responsible official of an eligible laboratory. To be eligible, the laboratory must be equipped to conduct certain standard ASTM tests for cement, concrete, concrete aggregates, or steel reinforcing bars. Policy established by NBS and ASTM at the formation of CCRL specifies that CCRL will not certify or rate laboratories nor serve as a referee in disputes concerning quality or properties of materials being tested. However, the policy regarding laboratory certification is currently undergoing review by the ASTM Joint C-1/C-9 Subcommittee on the CCRL, which along with NBS provides guidance on technical programs.

Geographically, the inspection work is organized into segments called tours. The approximate time involved in returning to a given area from one tour to the next is between two and two and one-half years. These tours have been numbered consecutively starting with Tour 1, which began in 1929, through Tour 24, which was completed in late 1986. The number of laboratories participating in inspection Tours 11 through 23 and the classification of these laboratories are listed in Table 1.

During the CCRL inspection, measurements of testing equipment are made to determine conformance with ASTM specifications. As an example, during the inspection of a cement testing laboratory, 50 items of equipment are compared to the applicable specifications and nine demonstrations of test procedures are witnessed. Some of the equipment measurements are recorded while others are noted as to whether or not they are within the prescribed limits of the specification. In the case of demonstration of test procedures, the nature of each deviation from the standard is noted. While the inspection is in progress, the inspectors bring to the attention of laboratory personnel each departure from the requirements of the standard that is noted so that on-the-spot adjustments may be made whenever possible. Other pertinent observations that may be of interest to the laboratory are also mentioned. At the completion of the inspection, a comprehensive oral report is presented to the laboratory supervisor or his representative. Within a short time after the inspection, a confirmatory written report is sent to the laboratory. This report is treated as confidential, but may be distributed to all interested parties designated by the inspected laboratory to receive such copies.

TABLE 1—Summary of participation in the CCRL inspection program.

	Tour 11	Tour 12	Tour 13	Tour 14	Tour 15	Tour 16	Tour 17	Tour 18	Tour 19	Tour 20	Tour 21	Tour 22	Tour 23
Tour Period	1954	1957	1960	1962	1964	1966	1968	1970	1972	1975	1977	1979	1982
Classification	1957	1960	1962	1964	1966	1968	1970	1972	1975	1977	1979	1982	1984
Cement Producer	165	170	188	201	195	184	165	186	186	190	183	186	164
Comm Testing Laboratory	24	45	56	107	120	131	138	161	225	201	213	261	274
Highway Department	39	43	50	59	61	57	59	61	60	56	56	55	57
School	4	2	6	0	0	0	1	0	1	0	1	0	0
Municipal	3	3	0	5	4	6	4	7	3	3	4	6	4
Federal	12	15	15	14	13	13	12	12	13	14	10	14	13
Concrete Products	...	...	...	...	27	22	20	24	31	27	30	41	37
Miscellaneous[a]	6	13	18	26	6	6	4	3	7	19	23	25	22
TOTAL INSPECTIONS	253	201	333	412	426	419	403	454	526	510	520	588	571
Cement Testing Labs	253	266	291	316	307	280	256	273	281	288	279	290	262
Concrete Testing Labs	98	131	151	223	251	261	258	293	359	339	349	414	419

[a]Includes producers of concrete products in Tour 11 through Tour 14.

Percent of Conformance Analyses

At the conclusion of each CCRL inspection tour, percentage of conformance data are compiled for test equipment inspected and procedures demonstrated. These statistics indicate the percentages of test demonstrations or equipment presented during the inspection which complied with the applicable standard. Tables 2 and 3 summarize the percentage of conformance data from the 21st, 22nd, and 23rd Tours for cement testing laboratories inspected. These compilations summarize the results of all participating laboratories without deviating from the confidentiality policy for individual laboratory results.

TABLE 2—*Summary of percentage of conformance for cement test equipment (CCRL Tours 21, 22, and 23).*

Item	21st Tour		22nd Tour		23rd Tour	
	No. Checked	Percent Conformance	No. Checked	Percent Conformance	No. Checked	Percent Conformance
Moist storage	280	76	299	78	258	79
Water storage	279	81	291	84	258	92
Mix water temperature	278	87	292	87	258	87
Mix room temperature	278	97	292	96	258	95
Mix room humidity	278	72	292	65	258	71
Turbidimeter	133	92	126	95	114	99
Analog microammeter	161	83	178	91	115	90
Digital microammeter	. . .	. . .	. . .	. . .	42	98
45-μm sieve	554	70	637	88	639	93
Wet sieve gage	259	96	274	92	256	97
Wet sieve spray nozzle	270	94	294	93	239	95
Autoclave	313	85	320	81	284	81
Autoclave gage	311	99	315	99	291	99
Comparator	279	97	287	97	263	97
Bar molds	1580	97	1670	97	1606	96
Graduates	209	98	262	92	244	96
Flow apparatus (w/flow)	302	85	311	85	287	85
Flow table	302	91	311	90	287	89
Flow mold	307	100	326	100	298	100
Flow calipers	301	98	313	98	287	100
Compression mach. ind.	285	93	289	84	244	84
bearing blocks	571	92	594	90	518	92
Cube molds	6123	95	5940	94	5618	95
Mix balances	360	91	365	93	324	96
Mix weights	2189	99	2162	99	1675	99
Vicat apparatus	448	98	479	98	437	98
Gillmore needles	287	99	294	97	260	100
Mechanical mixer	382	66	396	57	342	66
Air content apparatus	294	87	301	87	273	92
400 mL measures	321	91	338	93	312	94
Air permeability app.	318	78	346	73	299	83
Water retention equipment	152	93	151	93	136	89
Water retention dish	156	98	154	95	141	98
Miscellaneous	1904	. . .	2050	. . .	1929	. . .

SUMMARY

No. of items checked	20464		20949		.19050	
Average % conformance		94		90.1		.92.2

TABLE 3—*Summary of percentage of conformance for cement test procedures observed (CCRL Tours 21, 22, and 23).*

	21st Tour		22nd Tour		23rd Tour	
Item	No. Checked	Percent Conformance	No. Checked	Percent Conformance	No. Checked	Percent Conformance
Normal consistency	274	86	276	77	247	83
Vicat time of set	246	75	274	75	182	66
Gillmore time of set	240	70	188	60	156	71
Prep. of autoclave bar	265	80	266	88	222	94
Autoclave test	265	92	266	93	222	94
Air content determination	262	84	278	74	235	72
Cube/compression test	273	66	275	62	249	61
C430—fineness	245	91	249	86	225	78
Turbidimeter fineness	127	83	119	74	100	80
Air permeability	258	71	275	65	245	49
Early stiffness	276	72	223	75	207	80
		SUMMARY				
No. of demonstrations	2416		2689		2290	
Average % conformance		87		75		75

Evaluation of percentage of conformance data may be very useful in the following ways:

1. Initially, low percentage of conformance after a significant change in a standard specification or test method may result from a delay in obtaining current copies of the standards document, delays in acquiring new equipment required by the revised standard, or by inadequate training of laboratory personnel. However, the percentage of conformance generally improves with time until it reaches a limiting plateau. The CCRL inspection program is beneficial because it calls attention to and promotes conformance to such changes in standard specifications and test methods.

2. The percentage of conformance data could be evaluated by the responsible ASTM subcommittee to determine if an acceptable level of conformance has been reached. Unacceptably low levels as determined by the subcommittee would be an indication that there may be some problem with the standard.

3. The impact of changes in standards may be evaluated by monitoring the percentage of conformance before and after the change.

4. Historically, percentage of conformance data have also been used to determine the effect of various time intervals between CCRL inspections and of irregular participation by laboratories in the CCRL inspection program.

Overview of Proficiency Sample Programs

The distribution of samples of materials for comparative testing has been an activity of the CCRL since 1936. The proficiency test sample program involves preparing and shipping a slightly different pair of samples of a given material type to each participating laboratory. The laboratories run the appropriate tests on the samples and return the data to the CCRL, which then prepares statistical analyses. The current levels of laboratory participation in each of the four programs are: 252 laboratories for portland cement; 134 for blended cement; 92 for masonry cement; and 187 for portland cement concrete.

All four proficiency sample programs are similar. At intervals of either six or twelve months, quantities of two slightly different lots of a given material are procured, homogenized, and divided into two groups of individual test samples. Each participating laboratory receives a pair of samples (one from each group), performs the specified tests on each, and reports the results to CCRL. Within approximately two months after sample distribution, a final report is distributed to all participants. The report contains average values, standard deviations, scatter diagrams (Fig. 1), and other statistical information obtained using the procedures set forth in papers by Youden, Crandell, and Blaine [5,6,7]. Each laboratory can distinguish its test results but not the results of other laboratories. Summaries of the results obtained by a particular laboratory for specific proficiency testing programs are issued periodically in the form of performance charts to provide a clear picture of the laboratory's overall performance for the past ten pairs of samples (Fig. 2).

Final reports from the various CCRL proficiency sample programs are distributed routinely to the chairpersons of the appropriate ASTM C-1 and C-9 subcommittees for use in standards development. The raw data from all proficiency samples that have been distributed by CCRL are available in hard copy or on computer storage.

The portland cement program was the first CCRL proficiency sample activity, and there have been 40 pairs of samples distributed. These samples have been numbered consecutively with the most recent 40th sample pair including individual samples No. 79 and No. 80. Determinations for each sample involve testing for eleven physical properties and eleven chemical components

PORTLAND CEMENT SAMPLES, NUMBERS 69 AND 70

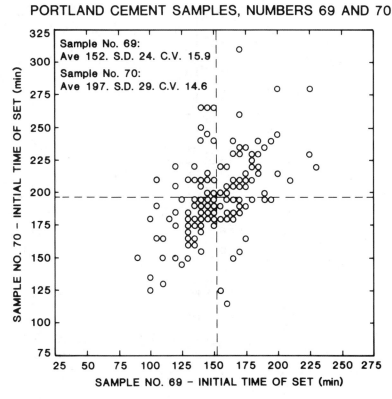

FIG. 1—*Youden* [5] *scatter diagram for initial time of set—Gillmore needles.*

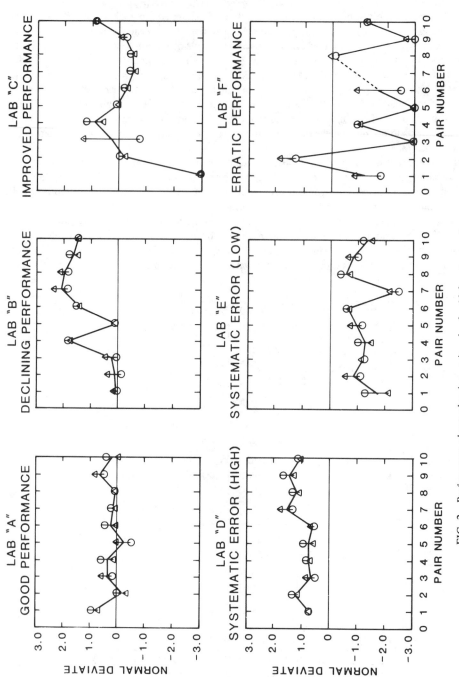

FIG. 2—*Performance charts showing various levels of laboratory performance over time.*

of cement. A participating laboratory may choose to do either one or both test series, and CCRL provides the necessary samples as appropriate. In addition, the laboratory may also choose to do rapid methods for chemical tests.

Application of CCRL Data

The data resulting from the CCRL inspection and proficiency sample programs may be used by standards committees in assessing the adequacy of current test methods, in determining the impact of revisions in standards, and as a basis for the development of precision statements. The first two of these uses of the data have already been discussed. A statistical procedure developed by ASTM Subcommittee C01.94 on Statistical Methods [8] and incorporated in ASTM Practice for Preparing Precision Statements for Test Methods for Construction Materials (C 670-84) provides a method for using CCRL proficiency sample results for formulation of precision statements. Pielert, Haverfield, and Spellerberg prepared estimates of precision for selected ASTM cement test methods based on this procedure, which may be considered by the appropriate ASTM subcommittees of Committee C-1 [9].

CCRL Technical Studies

The principal aim of technical studies conducted by CCRL is to develop information upon which revisions in standard specifications and methods of test, or changes in inspection procedures, might be based. These technical studies may be categorized as: (1) in-house studies conducted by CCRL staff; (2) cooperative studies with other NBS units; and (3) cooperative studies with organizations outside NBS.

In-House Technical Studies

Studies by CCRL staff may result from requests by ASTM technical committees or other interested organizations or from needs identified while conducting the laboratory inspection and proficiency sample programs. These studies fall into several categories:

Statistical Studies. The extensive CCRL data bases on cement and concrete testing going back to 1929 and 1948, respectively, provide opportunities for making significant improvements in standard methods of test. The development of estimates of precision statements for standards as discussed above is a primary application.

Changes to CCRL Programs. The CCRL programs have evolved over the years to meet the needs of the industries it serves. However, it is recognized that revisions or additions to the inspection and proficiency sample programs may be necessary to respond to changing needs. As an example, CCRL is currently studying the possible addition of pozzolan testing to the inspection program at the request of the ASTM Joint C-1/C-9 Subcommittee on the CCRL. Efforts are also being made to reduce the variability of test results in the proficiency sample program by evaluating the effect of several variables in the sample preparation process and in testing by the laboratories.

Application of On-Going CCRL Programs. The proficiency sample program has the potential for collecting additional data which could be of benefit in standards development. This could include having the laboratory record data which is not routinely collected while testing a proficiency sample, the performance of an additional test on a proficiency sample, the distribution of other material types (for example, cements from various sources) as part of the ongoing program, or special distributions of research samples for round-robin testing. However, since the primary function of the proficiency sample program is for the quality assurance of laboratory testing, any proposed research must be carefully evaluated as to its appropriateness and impact on on-going programs. Two examples will be discussed where the proficiency sample program was used to collect data related to ASTM C-1 standards.

45-μm (No. 325) Sieve Correction Factor (ASTM Method C 430). An example of an activity where additional data were collected on a proficiency sample is a study conducted to determine correction factors for the 45-μm sieve. The correction factors for the 45-μm sieve determined according to ASTM Standard Test Method for Fineness of Hydraulic Cement By The 45-μm (No. 325) Sieve (C 430-83) collected by CCRL during the inspection of laboratories cover a wide range. The distribution of correction factors in the sieves in current use was of additional interest because ASTM Subcommittee C01.25 on Cement Fineness was considering a proposal to limit the correction factors for the sieve. Since canvassing the proficiency sample program participants appeared to be a good mechanism to gather relevant data, the laboratories receiving portland cement Proficiency Samples No. 73 and No. 74 were asked to clean the 45-μm sieve according to ASTM Standard C 430 (Note 3), sieve a NBS Standard Reference Material (SRM)[3] and then sieve the proficiency samples provided by CCRL. The participants were requested to report whether they had cleaned the sieve, which NBS SRM was used, and the weights of the residues of the SRM and the CCRL samples. Correction factors were calculated for the sieves according to Section 4 of ASTM Standard C 430. The distribution of correction factors for sieves calibrated with NBS SRM 114N is shown in Fig. 3. The two peaks at correction factors of approximately 10 and 40% may suggest that there are two types of screen in general use. Figure 4 is a plot of residue of SRM 114N versus the portion of cement Proficiency Sample No. 74 retained. The two distinct groupings of results further support the suggestion that there are two different types of sieves in use. The results of this study were reported to ASTM Subcommittee C01.25.

Effect of Mold Release Agents on Cement Strength (ASTM Method C 109). The effect of various mold release agents on the strength of mortar cubes as tested by ASTM Test Method for Compressive Strength of Hydraulic Cement Mortars (Using 2-in. or 50-mm Cube Specimens) (C 109-86) has been of concern for some time. An appreciable variation has been found in the results when many laboratories test the same cements in the CCRL proficiency sample program. The standard deviations for Proficiency Samples 1 through 70 have ranged from 1.21 MPa (175 psi) to 2.33 MPa (339 psi) with many as high as 2.0 MPa (290 psi) [10]. ASTM C 109 prescribes that in preparing the molds to form 50-mm (2-in.) cubes "the faces of molds should be lightly coated with mineral oil or light cup grease" to facilitate removal of the specimens. This general specification has resulted in the use of many different types of mold release agents.

CCRL initiated a study in an attempt to determine the types of material being used and to identify, if possible, their effects on compressive strength. The study included the following activities:

(a) Previous CCRL studies were evaluated. The identity of mold release agents used by laboratories has been routinely gathered during CCRL inspections for many years. In 1961, Haverfield and Miracle studied the impact of animal fat release agents on strengths compared to the strengths obtained when using mineral oil [11]. It was determined that results of specimens using animal fat release agents were appreciably lower.

(b) Beginning in 1984, an attempt was made to relate information on types of release agents gathered during CCRL inspections to compressive strength data reported by participants in the portland cement proficiency sample program. Analysis of results indicates some correlation in the relationship between types of agents and strength, and it was determined that data were needed which more directly related release agent material to cement cube strengths. Program

---

[3]SRMs are well-characterized, homogeneous materials with specific physical or chemical properties certified by the National Bureau of Standards.

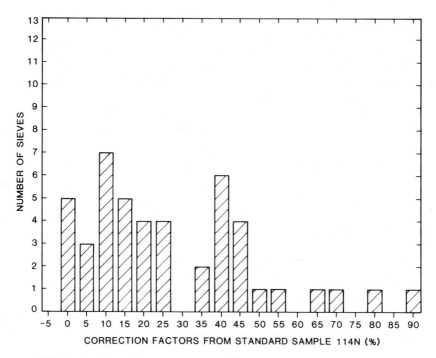

FIG. 3—*Distribution of correction factors for 45-μm sieve using NBS SRM 114N.*

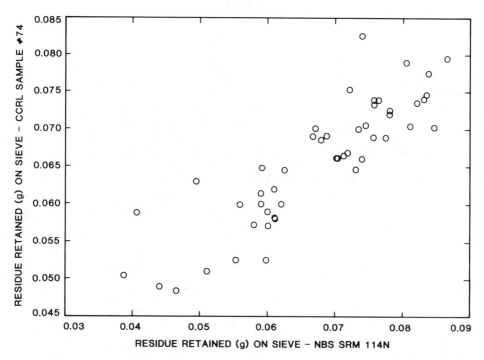

FIG. 4—*Residue retained on 45-μm sieve—NBS SRM 114N versus CCRL Sample 74.*

participants receiving portland cement Proficiency Samples No. 71 and No. 72 were asked to report what material(s) were used as release agents and the corresponding strength data. Analysis of these data indicated that it was not possible to predict the effect of various release agents on strength. This information was provided to Subcommittee C01.27 on Strength, and they initiated a program of cooperative tests among five laboratories. Samples of three release agents representing the range of possible effects on C 109 mortars were tested. Although the statistical analysis and a final report of the data has not been completed, it appears that the tests will provide a basis for improving the description of procedures in Method C 109 for oiling molds.

Cooperative Studies with NBS Units

CCRL is located organizationally within the NBS Building Materials Division, which conducts research on building materials, including cement and concrete, in the areas of service life prediction, quality assurance, and condition assessment. This provides the opportunity for CCRL staff to work closely with highly qualified researchers in addressing problems of common interest.

A current cooperative study addresses the chemical mechanism of the reaction between alkali-reactive aggregates and high-alkali cements in concrete. The project is led by Leslie Struble, Building Materials Division, and is supported by Curtis Spring and Edward Pennell of CCRL. This work involves expressing free water from the pores of hardened mortar specimens using a compression machine and conducting chemical analyses of the solutions. Visible light spectrophotometry, ion chromatography, and pH determinations are used in the analyses. The changes in the chemical composition of the pore solution throughout the hydration of the cement in the presence of the reactive aggregate provide information on the mechanism of the alkali-aggregate reaction. The same series of cements have been tested for expansion in a mortar bar series [12]. This research is of high interest to ASTM Subcommittees C01.32 on Alkali and C09.02.02 on Chemical Reactions of Aggregates in Concrete.

Cooperative Studies with Other Organizations

Organizations interested in the activities of CCRL occasionally come to CCRL to request assistance in carrying out technical studies. Cooperative research is currently underway with the National Sand and Gravel Association and the National Ready Mixed Concrete Association (NSGA/NRMCA) to evaluate the effect of reducing the number of specimens needed to determine compressive strength of cement as prescribed in ASTM C 109. Raymond Kolos of the CCRL and Richard Gaynor of the NSGA/NRMCA are using CCRL data to demonstrate how a reduction from three-cube batches to two-cube batches would affect results. The individual cube values from portland cement Proficiency Samples No. 75 and No. 76, as reported by the laboratory participants, are being used for this investigation. Table 4 summarizes the effect on coefficient of variation of testing two cubes from a batch instead of three cubes as currently required in Section 11.1 of C 109. The variation for a two-cube batch compares very favorably

TABLE 4—*Difference in coefficient of variation if two cubes are broken at each age instead of three cubes (ASTM C 109).*

Testing Type	3-Day Tests		7-Day Tests	
	Avg. 3	Avg. 2	Avg. 3	Avg. 2
Multilab	6.92	6.97	6.23	6.28
Single-operator	3.97	4.05	3.69	3.77

with a three-cube batch. The detailed results of this investigation will be published separately and provided to the appropriate C-1 subcommittee.

Conclusions

This paper has highlighted the scope of the data available at CCRL and the type of technical support available to the standards committees of ASTM. The benefits arising from the CCRL programs described in this paper are: (1) improving the reliability of test measurements; (2) providing data to quantify standard measurement techniques; and (3) providing direct communication between construction materials testing laboratories and the standards-writing committees. CCRL collects valuable information which is currently being effectively used in support of standards development for cement and concrete.

References

[1] Locke, J. W. and Pielert, J. H., *"Evaluation and Accreditation of Construction Materials Laboratories,"* Conference on Quality Assurance of Highways and Bridges, National Bureau of Standards, Washington, DC, August 1983.
[2] Steele, G. W., "Quality Assurance for Our Highways—The AASHTO Materials Reference Laboratory (AMRL)—Fifteen Years of Service," *AASHTO Quarterly,* Vol. 60, No. 1, 1981, p. 35.
[3] Dise, J. R., "Fiftieth Anniversary of the Cement and Concrete Reference Laboratory," *Concrete International: Design and Construction,* Volume VI, No. 10, Oct. 1979, pp. 100–105.
[4] Pielert, J. H., "An Update—The Cement and Concrete Reference Laboratory," *Concrete International,* November 1984, pp. 55–56.
[5] Youden, W. J., "Statistical Aspects of the Cement Testing Program," *Proceedings,* American Society for Testing and Materials, Vol. 59, 1959, p. 1120.
[6] Crandall, J. R. and Blaine, R. L., "Statistical Evaluation of Interlaboratory Cement Tests," *Proceedings,* American Society for Testing and Materials, Vol. 59, 1959, p. 1129.
[7] Youden, W. J., "The Collaborative Test," *Journal of the Association of Official Agricultural Chemists,* Vol. 46, 1963, pp. 55–62.
[8] ASTM Subcommittee C01.94 on Statistical Methods, "Use of CCRL Reference Sample Results for Precision Statements," *Cement, Concrete, and Aggregates,* Vol. 2, No. 1, Summer 1980, pp. 50–52.
[9] Pielert, J. H., Haverfield, J. W., and Spellerberg, P. A. "Application of CCRL Data in the Formulation of Precision Estimates for Selected Cement Standards," *Cement, Concrete, Aggregates,* Vol. 7, No. 1, Summer 1985, pp. 37–42.
[10] Haverfield, J. W., Kolos, R. M., and Haupt, R. K., Compilation of Statistics from the CCRL Portland Cement Reference Sample Program (Communication to C-1 Committee), 7 Jan. 1984.
[11] Internal CCRL Memorandum, April 1961.
[12] Struble, L. and Diamond, S., "Influence of Cement Alkali Distribution on Expansion Due to Alkali-Silica Reaction," in *Alkalies in Concrete, ASTM STP 930,* V. Dobson, Ed., American Society for Testing and Materials, Philadelphia, 1986, pp. 31–45.

Luc R. Taerwe[1]

Detection of Inherent Heterogeneities in Cement Strength Records by Means of Segmentation

REFERENCE: Taerwe, L. R., **"Detection of Inherent Heterogeneities in Cement Strength Records by Means of Segmentation,"** *Uniformity of Cement Strength, ASTM STP 961*, E. Farkas and P. Klieger, Eds., American Society for Testing and Materials, Philadelphia, 1987, pp. 42–65.

ABSTRACT: Five series of cement strength data are analyzed by means of an appropriate segmentation technique, which makes it possible to detect inherent heterogeneities hidden in these records. This heterogeneous aspect follows from the fact that the mean strength level presents a step-wise variation in time, rather than a continuous one. It is indicated that the variation of the mean value of the segments contributes significantly to the total variance of the strength records. Finally, it is mentioned that a similar model is applicable to concrete strength records.

KEY WORDS: cement strength, segmentation, statistical analysis

Usually the statistical analysis of cement strength records is limited to the determination of the mean value and the standard deviation of strength data obtained during a fixed period. Often it is verified whether the observations belong to a normal population, as almost all common statistical production control techniques, for example, control charts, are based on the normality assumption.

However, it appears to be very useful to consider cement strength not merely as a random variable, but to extend the analysis with an investigation of the evolution of cement strength in time. Although cement production is submitted to very intensive production control and cement strength records present a rather low standard deviation, a thorough analysis makes it possible to detect inherent heterogeneities hidden in these records.

In the following study, an appropriate segmentation technique is used that makes it possible to subdivide strength records in segments and to build a model that represents the basic stochastic structure of cement strength in time.

Survey of the Analyzed Strength Data

The analysis is performed on five series of strength data arranged in chronological order. The individual values are mentioned in the Appendix. The samples are taken at four different Belgian cement production plants during the same period of four years (208 weeks). The main characteristics of the five series, including sample rates, are listed in Table 1.

The results of Series C1 to C4 were determined at 28 days. Strength data obtained at three days at one of the plants are also considered in order to investigate to what extent the nature of the variation, which will be subsequently modeled, is related to the production process. Thus

---

[1]Assistant, Magnel Laboratory for Reinforced Concrete, Ghent State University, B-9710 Ghent, Belgium.

TABLE 1—*General survey of the series.*

Series	Age of Testing, Days	N	Mean Value, MPa (psi)	Standard Deviation, MPa (psi)	Coefficient of Variation, %	Mean Sample Rate Per Week[a]	Fraction Below 40 MPa
C1	28	556	51.4 (7455)	3.51 (509)	6.8	2.67	5.8 10^{-4}
C2	28	437	56.7 (8223)	3.08 (447)	5.4	2.10	3.0 10^{-8}
C3	28	536	52.0 (7542)	2.64 (383)	5.1	2.58	2.8 10^{-6}
C4	28	402	47.4 (6874)	3.53 (512)	7.4	1.93	1.8 10^{-2}
C4′	3	402	28.4 (4119)	3.49 (506)	12.3	1.93	

NOTE: N = total number of tests per series.
[a]Calculated as $N/208$.

the test data grouped in Series C4′ and C4 result from specimens made from the same standardized mortar mix, but tested respectively at 3 and 28 days.

As the minimum required compressive strength at 28 days equals 40 MPa (5801 psi), the fraction below this value, assuming a Gaussian strength distribution, is also indicated in Table 1.

In Belgium, cement strength values are determined according to the European Standard EN 196: "Methods of Testing Cement—Determination of Strength" (Part 1). Prisms with dimensions 40 by 40 by 160 mm are first tested in bending, and on the two resulting halves a compression test is executed. The strength values that are used for the analysis represent the mean of six individual values resulting from three prisms. The specimens are made with cement taken from grab samples of about 10 kg. Per week of production, at least two grab samples are taken. Although the test method differs from the one mentioned in the ASTM C 109 standard [Test Method for Compressive Strength of Hydraulic Cement Mortars (Using 2-in. or 50-mm Cube Specimens) (C 109–86)], it is deemed that owing to this the basic conclusions of this paper are not invalidated.

The testing standard deviations, mentioned in Table 2, are evaluated as follows. The Belgian Research Institute of the Cement Industry has sent every week, for one year, a reference cement sample to each of the four testing laboratories. The reference cement is stored in special conditions in order to make sure that no changes of its properties take place. Each laboratory makes a test specimen with the reference cement and executes the compression test at 28 days. Over a period of one year, 52 test results become available for each testing laboratory. The standard deviations of these 52 values are mentioned in Table 2. They include only the variations that may result from making the specimens, curing, and testing since the intrinsic properties of the cement remain constant.

TABLE 2—*Testing standard deviations for different laboratories.*

Laboratory	Testing Standard Deviation, MPa (psi)
1	1.14 (165)
2	1.46 (212)
3	0.85 (123)
4	1.75 (254)

The Mean Square Successive Difference

General

For a sample of n consecutive observations $x_i (i = 1, \ldots, n)$, the mean square successive difference δ^2 is defined as ([1-2])

$$\delta^2 = \frac{1}{n-1} \sum_{i=1}^{n-1} (x_{i+1} - x_i)^2 \tag{1}$$

In the case of a normal population, the quantity

$$q^2 = \frac{\delta^2}{2} \tag{2}$$

is an unbiased estimate of σ^2 with efficiency equal to

$$\frac{\text{Var}[s^2]}{\text{Var}[q^2]} = \frac{2(n-1)}{3n-4} = \frac{2}{3}\left(1 + \frac{1}{3n-4}\right) \tag{3}$$

where

$$s^2 = \frac{1}{n-1} \sum_{i=1}^{n} (x_i - \bar{x})^2 \tag{4}$$

The efficiency of q^2 as an estimate of σ^2 equals 1 for $n = 2$ and approaches 2/3 for $n \to \infty$.

The use of q^2 is particularly useful when the mean of the population, from which the observations are successively drawn, exhibits gradual or stepwise changes, the variance remaining constant. In that case the estimate s^2 of σ^2 will tend to be too large because s^2 also includes the variation of the population mean. If, during the observation period, a change in population mean takes place, the effect of this change on the estimate q^2 will be relatively small since q^2 includes only the differences between successive values, and generally only one difference will be rather high. Therefore, the estimate s^2 is much more sensitive to changes in the population mean than is the estimate q^2.

If we take as null hypothesis that the population mean μ remains constant during the observation period, and as an alternative that μ changes in one way or another, we can make use of the test statistic

$$r = \frac{q^2}{s^2} \tag{5}$$

small values of r being significant. It can be shown that

$$E[r] = 1 \text{ and } \text{Var}[r] = \frac{1}{n+1}\left(1 - \frac{1}{n-1}\right) \tag{6}$$

Some fractiles in the distribution of r are mentioned in Ref 2. For $n > 20$, r is approximately normally distributed so that the α-fractile can be calculated as

$$r_\alpha \simeq 1 + \frac{u_\alpha}{\sqrt{n+1}}$$ (7)

u_α being the α-fractile in the standardized normal distribution.

Application

For the five complete series, values of s, q, and r are mentioned in Table 3. It appears that r is always lower than the 1% fractile of the distribution of r, and hence the null hypothesis is rejected. This means that significant changes occur in the mean strength level.

Hald [3] uses r to test whether a production process is in the state of statistical control. By coincidence, he uses consecutive cement strength values to illustrate the procedure and finds a significant r-value. He concludes: "Hence, the quality of the cement is not under statistical control and assignable causes influencing the quality figures may be found in the manufacturing process itself or in the conditions under which the laboratory control of the strength is carried out."

The foregoing investigation suggests that the processes which produce the strength results listed in the Appendix can hardly be considered as being "under control" in the *classical* statistical sense. However, this remark mainly holds for short-term variations and not for the long-term behavior. This statement is not meant as criticism on the current production methods, but shows that in practice it is very difficult to obtain a production process with perfectly homogeneous output properties. This comment is also applicable to other types of production processes and for many time-dependent phenomena that are influenced by random disturbances.

Development of the Stochastic Model

Introduction

Once it is found that the population mean doesn't remain stable at short term, it is attractive to find out what part of the total variation is due to these changes. In fact, we want to dispose of a rational procedure to divide the strength records into subgroups such that the conditions are essentially the same within each subgroup. However, in this case we have no prior knowledge of the occurrence of assignable causes of variation in the mean level. A possible way to proceed is to divide a record into subgroups of equal size n. However, the choice of n is quite arbitrary and the estimated values of the variances within and between subgroups depend on the chosen length of the subgroups. Hence it is necessary to develop an appropriate stochastic model and an associated practical estimation procedure.

TABLE 3—*Calculated values of* s, q, *and* r *for different series.*

Series	N	s According to Eq 4 with $n = N$, MPa (psi)	q According to Eq 2 with $n = N$, MPa (psi)	$r = \dfrac{q^2}{s^2}$	$r_{0.01}$
C1	556	3.51 (509)	1.96 (284)	0.310	0.901
C2	437	3.08 (447)	2.41 (350)	0.612	0.889
C3	536	2.64 (383)	1.50 (218)	0.320	0.900
C4	402	3.53 (512)	2.63 (381)	0.555	0.884
C4′	402	3.49 (506)	2.58 (374)	0.548	0.884

Description of the Model

In the sequel, the evolution in time of the cement production process is investigated. This is performed on the basis of the evolution of consecutive strength values, determined on prisms made with cement samples and taken in chronological order from a given production unit. For the sake of clearness, it is emphasized in this paper that we consider strength at a given age. Hence, by the term "time aspect" we do not mean the increase in strength of a given specimen in time, but the variation in strength of different specimens made consecutively during production.

To build up the model, we premise that the mean strength level does not vary in a continuous way but rather in a discontinuous one and that it presents jumps at certain points in time. In between these jumps, the mean level remains constant. Whether these jumps are caused by the production process itself, or follow from a similar behavior of the input variables, is not investigated here. The unknown causes of variability which disturb the mean strength level are usually called assignable causes [3]. Thus, a series of successive observations of strength consists of consecutive subgroups, each group corresponding to a certain mean strength level that remains constant in between the mentioned jumps. Each subgroup, which may be considered as a subpopulation, is called a "segment." The number of test results in Segment j is denoted T_j, the mean value of the T_j results is denoted m_j, and the standard deviation of the T_j-values with respect to m_j is denoted s_j (Fig. 1). The distinction between consecutive segments is made on the basis of jumps in the mean strength level, although the standard deviation, too, may show a similar piecewise constant evolution (Fig. 1). In the theory of stochastic processes this type of

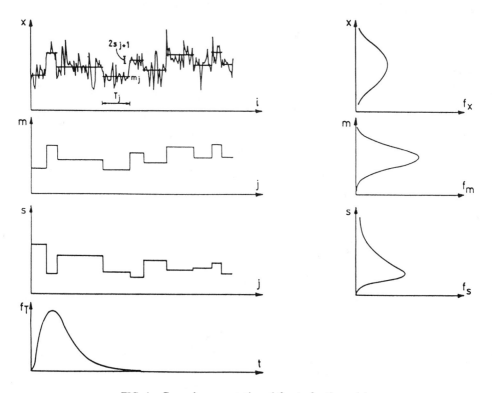

FIG. 1—*General representation of the stochastic model.*

behavior is called a "renewal pulse process." The individual values of the random variable X (here cement strength) arise from random variations which are superimposed on a step-function. The complete model is fully determined by the distribution functions of the random variables m, s, and T.

Segmentation Technique

In Ref 4, a method is developed to subdivide a record into segments by making use of the mean square successive difference and a likelihood function. In the following paragraphs, a brief survey of the segmentation technique is presented. More details may be found in Ref 4. The procedure consists of three stages.

In the first stage, a first estimate of the length of the different segments is found by running through the series in chronological order. A minimum segment length of $T_0 = 4$ observations is assumed. For the first four values, s, q, and r are calculated according to Eqs 4, 2, and 5. It is checked whether $r < r_{0.05}$ for T_0 observations, that is, whether r is in the critical region of the test outlined in one of the previous sections. If $r < r_{0.05}$, T_0 is taken as estimate of the length of the first segment. If $r > r_{0.05}$, the next value is added to the segment, s, q, and r are calculated for $T_0 + 1$ observations, and it is checked again whether $r < r_{0.05}$. In the affirmative case the segment is considered as being ended and the procedure is repeated for the next segment. In this way a first segmentation is performed.

In the second stage, the series is run through not in chronological but in reversed order, which yields a configuration of segments which will be slightly different from the previous one. These first two stages are performed automatically by means of a suitable computer program.

In the third stage, the "optimal" configuration is looked for by an interactive computer program which needs some decisions to be taken by the operator. The final configuration is optimal in the sense that it maximizes the likelihood function of the complete series. The likelihood function L is calculated as follows, assuming that the observations in each segment are independently normally distributed and omitting the factor $1/\sqrt{2\pi}$

$$L \sim \prod_{j=1}^{n_s} \prod_{i=1}^{T_j} \frac{1}{s_j'} \cdot \exp\left[-\frac{1}{2}\left(\frac{x_i - m_j}{s_j'}\right)^2\right] \tag{8}$$

or

$$-\ln L \sim \sum_{j=1}^{n_s}\left[T_j s_j' + \frac{1}{2 s_j'^2} \sum_{i=1}^{T_j}(x_i - m_j)^2\right] \tag{9}$$

where

L = likelihood function for a complete series,
n_s = number of segments in a series,
T_j = number of observations in Segment j ($j = 1, \ldots, n_s$),
x_i = i-th observation in Segment j ($i = 1, \ldots, T_j$),
$m_j = (\Sigma x_i)/T_j$, and
$s_j' = \sqrt{(\Sigma(x_i - m_j)^2/T_j)}$.

The boundaries of the segments are adjusted until the maximum of Eq 8 or the minimum of Eq 9 is reached. When it is necessary to choose between two configurations with a different number of segments, use is made of an appropriate likelihood ratio test ([4,5]).

Results of the Segmentation

In Figs. 2 and 3, the first 200 values of Series C2 and C4 are represented. These fragments correspond to time periods of about 103 and 95 weeks, respectively. The upper part of both figures shows the records as sampled. The empirical points, that are represented in chronological order, are connected by straight lines. In the middle part of the figures, the results of the segmentation are shown. The mean value of each segment is indicated by a horizontal line. The standard deviation is given in the lower part of the figures, on the same scale but with shifted origin.

These two examples were chosen because of their different global appearance. Indeed, in Fig. 3 it is possible to discover some sinusoidal basic variation, whereas in Fig. 2 this type of variation is only weakly present. This aspect is discussed further on.

Tables 4, 5, and 6 provide the main characteristics of the empirical distributions of m, s, and T. The number of segments per series is denoted n_s.

When the usual statistical tests concerning the difference between the means of two series of observations (see, for example, Ref 3) are applied to consecutive segments, it appears that their mean values are significantly different.

Discussion of the Results

General Characteristics

Although the analyzed series come from four different production units, several common characteristics appear from the tables summarizing the segmentation results.

1. The ratio of the variance of m (= square of the standard deviation mentioned in Table 4) to the total variance (= square of the standard deviation mentioned in Table 1) ranges between 0.63 and 0.86.

2. The coefficient of variation of s is about 30%.

3. The mean value of T varies between 15 and 23, which corresponds to a mean segment length of eight weeks if the different sample rates are taken into account.

4. The coefficient of variation of T is about 65%.

Analysis of Variance

1. As just mentioned, the ratio of the variance of m to the total variance ranges between 0.63 and 0.86. This indicates that the variation of m is important with respect to the total strength variation. From a variance ratio test (F-test), it even follows that the mentioned variances are not significantly different.

2. The main sources of variation can be classified in two groups:

(*a*) Variation coming from the manufacturing or production process.

(*b*) Variation resulting from specimen preparation, specimen curing, and strength testing.

Let us call the first type "variation due to production" and the second type "variation due to testing." In the present case it is not possible to distinguish exactly between both sources with respect to the contributions to the total variance, nor to the jumps in the mean level. However, some useful indications follow from the following comparisons.

3. The testing standard deviation mentioned in Table 2 is significantly lower than the standard deviation of the means mentioned in Table 4 and even lower than the mean within segment standard deviation mentioned in Table 5. Hence, a considerable part of the variation of m must be due to the production process itself.

4. Series C4 and C4' have almost the same mean value of T, and most of the other statistical characteristics, except of course for the global mean strength level, are also very comparable. This means that curing and testing only moderately influence the values of the parameters of the model, which is in agreement with the magnitude of the testing standard deviations mentioned in Table 2.

Relation to Concrete Strength

In Ref 4, this type of modelling was originally applied to concrete strength records, and one of the aims of this paper is to show its validity for cement strength records. Since the origin of the cement that has been used on the concrete plants mentioned in Ref 4 is not known, strictly speaking no direct relationship can be established between the analyzed cement and concrete strength series. However, as both types of results date from the same period and are of Belgian origin, it is suggested that the stochastic model for cement strength, as described in the foregoing sections, is partly transmitted to the concrete strength model via the concrete production plant.

With respect to the practical verification of this model, it would be very useful if really occurring jumps in the concrete strength level could be associated with previous new cement supplies or simultaneous jumps in the cement strength level. However, this type of verification turns out to be very difficult in practice due to the fact that the exact division of raw material supplies between different production units, within one concrete plant, is mostly difficult to follow.

Final Remarks

1. As in every statistical estimation or hypothesis testing problem, the conclusions to some extent depend on the confidence levels that are adopted. This particularly holds for the figures just mentioned. However, when the final purpose is to compare the results of different series, each obtained with the same confidence levels, this aspect is of minor importance. In a more refined analysis, different types of distribution functions can be fitted to the data mentioned in Tables 4, 5, and 6. In this way the proposed model can be applied in probabilistic reliability studies and quality assurance programs.

2. In the author's opinion, the presented way of analysis allows detection of the basic characteristics of a production process, including of course variations due to testing. It is clear that this type of analysis is more fundamental than procedures which make use of constant subgroup lengths as is, for example, the case when running means are considered.

3. It was already mentioned that some type of periodic behavior, which could be associated with seasonal influences, might also be present in the series. This was intentionally not investigated for these series because we didn't want to model long-term behavior but rather the basic medium-term fluctuations. Of course, when one would make a graph of the consecutive m-values in function of time, some ups and downs will appear. However, for a single record this behavior need not be strictly periodic. This aspect is different when one works on a yearly basis and looks for the mean of records of several years (one decade, for example). In that case a more pronounced seasonal behavior will probably appear.

Conclusions

On the basis of the analysis of five series of cement strength values arranged in chronological order, a stochastic model for the variation of consecutive strength values in time is proposed. The basic feature of this model is that the mean strength level does not vary in a continuous way, but presents sudden jumps, which indicates the existence of inherent heterogeneities in cement strength records.

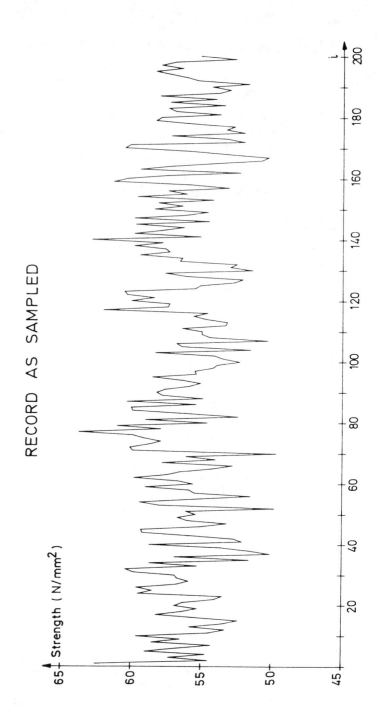

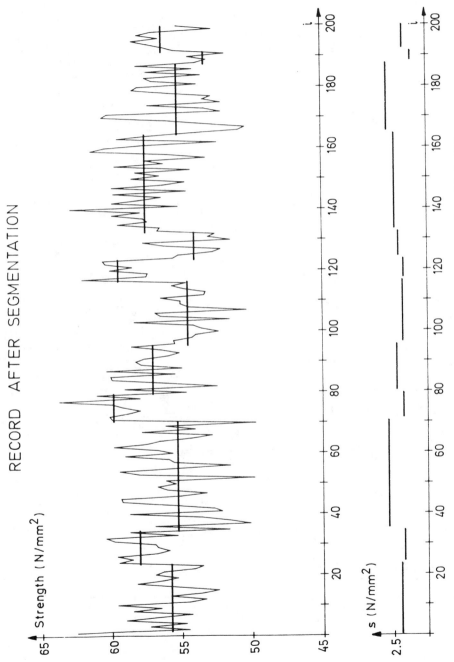

FIG. 2—Cement strength record as sampled and after segmentation (part of Series C2).

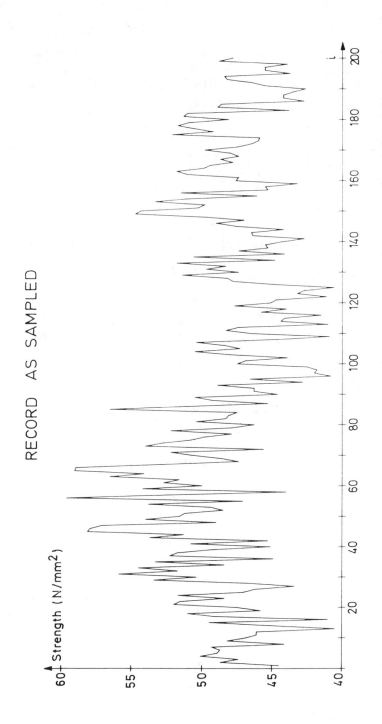

RECORD AS SAMPLED

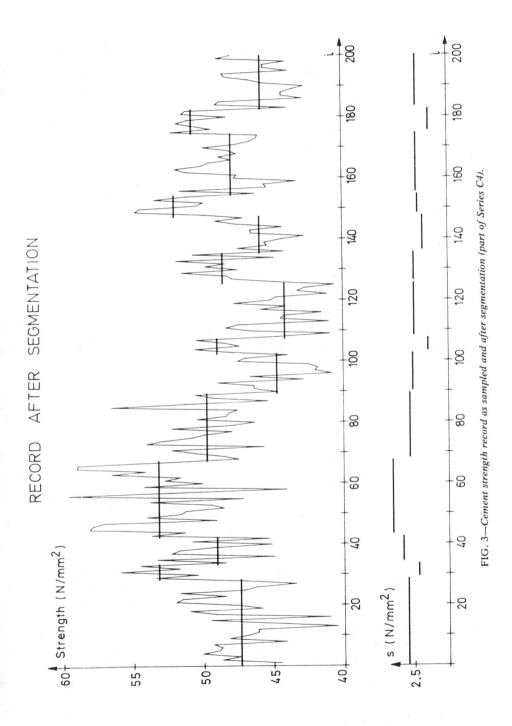

FIG. 3—*Cement strength record as sampled and after segmentation (part of Series C4).*

TABLE 4—*Distribution of* m.

Series	n_s	Mean Value, MPa (psi)	Standard Deviation, MPa (psi)	Coefficient of Variation, %
C1	34	51.4 (7455)	3.25 (471)	6.3
C2	26	56.9 (8252)	2.52 (365)	4.4
C3	23	51.9 (7527)	2.24 (325)	4.3
C4	27	47.8 (6923)	2.81 (408)	5.9
C4′	26	28.4 (4119)	3.00 (435)	10.6

NOTE: n_s = total number of segments in each series.

TABLE 5—*Distribution of* s.

Series	n_s	Mean Value, MPa (psi)	Standard Deviation, MPa (psi)	Coefficient of Variation, %
C1	34	1.75 (254)	0.43 (62)	24.4
C2	26	2.09 (303)	0.54 (78)	25.7
C3	23	1.29 (187)	0.40 (58)	31.2
C4	27	2.22 (322)	0.85 (123)	38.4
C4′	26	2.14 (310)	0.83 (120)	38.9

TABLE 6—*Distribution of* T.

Series	n_s	Mean Value	Standard Deviation	Coefficient of Variation, %
C1	34	16.4	11.0	67.0
C2	26	16.8	11.0	65.5
C3	23	23.3	14.8	63.3
C4	27	14.9	8.9	58.3
C4′	26	15.5	11.1	71.8

By means of appropriate statistical methods, the records may be split up into segments with variable length. It appears that the variance of the mean of the segments contributes considerably to the total variance. The mean value of the length of the segments ranges between 15 and 23 observations.

The proposed analysis allows identification of the basic structure of the output of a cement production plant on the basis of cement strength values.

It was shown elsewhere (Ref *4*) that this type of model is also valid for concrete strength.

Acknowledgment

The author is very much indebted to Y. Dechamps, director of the Belgian Research Institute of the Cement Industry, for providing the experimental values.

APPENDIX

Table A1

Series C1 (N = 556)

1	49.0	63	50.0	125	47.0	187	55.0	249	50.0	311	50.0	373	50.0	435	54.0	497	60.0
2	51.0	64	50.0	126	47.0	188	54.0	250	56.0	312	50.0	374	50.0	436	52.0	498	54.5
3	49.0	65	55.0	127	48.0	189	55.0	251	55.0	313	53.0	375	51.0	437	55.0	499	50.0
4	49.0	66	52.0	128	47.0	190	54.0	252	51.0	314	51.0	376	50.0	438	54.0	500	52.0
5	51.0	67	53.0	129	46.0	191	53.0	253	53.0	315	51.0	377	45.0	439	52.0	501	55.0
6	49.0	68	53.0	130	48.0	192	51.0	254	57.0	316	52.0	378	51.0	440	56.0	502	52.0
7	51.0	69	54.0	131	52.0	193	53.0	255	53.0	317	50.0	379	45.0	441	50.0	503	54.0
8	52.5	70	51.0	132	45.0	194	55.0	256	53.0	318	51.0	380	50.0	442	50.0	504	55.0
9	52.0	71	48.0	133	51.0	195	55.0	257	49.0	319	51.0	381	50.0	443	53.0	505	56.0
10	50.0	72	46.5	134	49.0	196	53.0	258	54.0	320	50.0	382	49.0	444	49.0	506	56.0
11	51.0	73	50.0	135	48.0	197	54.0	259	50.0	321	51.0	383	48.0	445	53.0	507	55.0
12	51.0	74	48.0	136	43.0	198	56.0	260	52.0	322	51.0	384	50.0	446	52.0	508	50.0
13	49.0	75	48.0	137	54.0	199	55.0	261	52.0	323	49.0	385	47.0	447	52.0	509	53.0
14	49.0	76	46.0	138	52.0	200	55.0	262	51.0	324	49.0	386	47.0	448	53.0	510	55.0
15	48.0	77	50.0	139	49.0	201	54.0	263	53.0	325	47.0	387	47.0	449	53.0	511	51.0
16	47.0	78	50.0	140	49.0	202	56.0	264	50.0	326	45.0	388	49.0	450	53.0	512	53.0
17	52.0	79	48.0	141	47.0	203	55.0	265	52.0	327	47.0	389	45.0	451	54.0	513	55.0
18	52.0	80	48.0	142	48.0	204	51.0	266	51.0	328	46.0	390	46.0	452	54.0	514	52.0
19	53.0	81	48.0	143	53.0	205	53.0	267	53.0	329	50.0	391	46.0	453	53.0	515	50.0
20	52.0	82	46.0	144	51.0	206	51.0	268	50.0	330	46.0	392	47.0	454	57.0	516	56.0
21	50.0	83	47.0	145	54.0	207	52.0	269	48.0	331	49.0	393	46.0	455	54.0	517	53.0
22	53.0	84	46.0	146	53.0	208	54.0	270	48.0	332	48.0	394	45.0	456	55.0	518	53.0
23	53.0	85	45.0	147	55.0	209	54.0	271	47.0	333	48.0	395	46.0	457	57.0	519	52.0
24	48.0	86	47.0	148	53.0	210	52.0	272	49.0	334	48.0	396	49.0	458	50.0	520	54.0
25	44.0	87	43.0	149	52.0	211	52.0	273	48.0	335	46.0	397	51.0	459	50.0	521	52.0
26	51.0	88	46.0	150	51.0	212	52.0	274	50.0	336	44.0	398	50.0	460	50.0	522	55.0
27	47.0	89	47.0	151	50.0	213	55.0	275	46.0	337	49.0	399	51.0	461	54.0	523	53.0
28	49.0	90	51.0	152	53.0	214	56.0	276	53.0	338	47.0	400	51.0	462	54.0	524	54.0
29	51.0	91	47.0	153	51.0	215	55.0	277	54.0	339	50.0	401	47.0	463	52.0	525	55.0

Table A1—*Continued.*

Series C1 (N = 556)

30	49.0	92	43.0	154	52.0	216	52.0	278	47.0	340	50.0	402	51.0	464	49.0	526	54.0
31	47.0	93	48.0	155	53.0	217	53.0	279	50.0	341	49.0	403	49.0	465	50.0	527	51.0
32	50.0	94	45.0	156	53.0	218	51.0	280	55.0	342	51.0	404	54.0	466	50.0	528	54.0
33	49.0	95	47.0	157	54.0	219	56.0	281	55.0	343	50.0	405	46.0	467	52.0	529	55.0
34	49.0	96	45.5	158	49.0	220	52.0	282	52.0	344	51.0	406	50.0	468	56.0	530	57.0
35	49.0	97	45.0	159	54.0	221	54.0	283	51.0	345	53.0	407	48.0	469	56.0	531	50.0
36	49.0	98	49.0	160	52.0	222	53.5	384	54.0	346	49.0	408	47.0	470	58.0	532	58.0
37	51.0	99	51.0	161	50.0	223	51.0	285	53.0	347	53.0	409	52.0	471	60.0	533	59.0
38	49.0	100	44.0	162	48.0	224	54.0	286	52.0	348	52.0	410	52.0	472	60.0	534	55.0
39	50.0	101	48.5	163	48.0	225	53.0	287	56.0	349	53.0	411	47.0	473	60.0	535	58.0
40	52.0	102	48.0	164	52.0	226	51.0	288	57.0	350	49.0	412	52.0	474	59.0	536	56.0
41	50.0	103	44.0	165	51.0	227	52.0	289	55.0	351	52.0	413	54.0	475	62.0	537	57.0
42	52.0	104	43.0	166	49.0	228	52.0	290	55.0	352	51.0	414	47.0	476	61.0	538	55.0
43	49.0	105	45.0	167	54.0	229	54.0	291	56.0	353	49.0	415	48.0	477	59.0	539	51.0
44	51.0	106	46.0	168	53.0	230	51.0	292	51.0	354	48.0	416	51.0	478	58.0	540	59.0
45	49.0	107	46.0	169	56.0	231	55.0	293	50.0	355	50.0	417	57.0	479	56.0	541	57.0
46	50.0	108	47.5	170	50.0	232	56.0	294	52.0	356	50.0	418	57.0	480	55.0	542	55.0
47	46.0	109	44.0	171	49.0	233	52.0	295	51.0	357	50.0	419	55.0	481	62.0	543	54.0
48	46.0	110	46.0	172	45.0	234	54.0	296	52.0	358	45.0	420	55.0	482	56.5	544	58.0
49	51.0	111	45.0	173	48.0	235	53.0	297	50.0	359	49.0	421	53.0	483	57.0	545	54.0
50	51.0	112	47.0	174	46.0	236	53.0	298	49.0	360	55.0	422	58.0	484	57.0	546	56.0
51	52.0	113	45.0	175	48.0	237	50.0	299	49.0	361	53.0	423	56.0	485	58.0	547	55.0
52	51.0	114	45.0	176	56.0	238	58.0	300	50.0	362	53.0	424	53.0	486	53.0	548	54.0
53	51.0	115	46.0	177	54.0	239	56.0	301	53.0	363	51.0	425	53.0	487	53.0	549	54.0
54	49.0	116	45.0	178	58.0	240	55.5	302	51.0	364	50.0	426	53.0	488	52.0	550	57.0
55	49.0	117	51.0	179	53.0	241	55.0	303	52.0	365	51.0	427	53.0	489	54.0	551	56.0
56	49.0	118	52.0	180	53.0	242	54.0	304	51.0	366	51.0	428	54.0	490	50.0	552	58.0
57	49.0	119	49.0	181	48.0	243	52.0	305	51.0	367	47.0	429	58.0	491	49.0	553	53.9
58	49.5	120	51.0	182	52.0	244	51.0	306	53.0	368	46.0	430	54.0	492	55.0	554	54.0
59	51.0	121	51.0	183	50.0	245	49.0	307	51.0	369	45.0	431	56.0	493	55.0	555	52.0
60	52.0	122	46.0	184	49.0	246	52.0	308	50.0	370	46.0	432	56.0	494	57.0	556	57.0
61	49.0	123	51.0	185	55.0	247	48.0	309	48.0	371	45.0	433	56.0	495	58.0		
62	53.0	124	49.5	186	55.0	248	50.0	310	51.0	372	44.0	434	53.0	496	57.0		

Table A2

Series C2 (N = 437)

1	62.5	50	55.4	99	53.9	148	56.2	197	57.9	246	55.3	295	58.9	344	55.9	393	55.2
2	54.5	51	56.1	100	52.3	149	54.6	198	56.9	247	57.9	296	57.5	345	55.7	394	54.9
3	57.3	52	49.8	101	53.5	150	58.4	199	52.6	248	58.8	297	60.9	346	55.0	395	50.5
4	54.7	53	58.0	102	54.1	151	56.4	200	55.1	249	57.5	298	59.2	347	59.6	396	51.9
5	59.0	54	59.4	103	58.3	152	58.1	201	50.5	250	55.6	299	57.7	348	62.9	397	58.4
6	56.8	55	55.6	104	51.5	153	54.2	202	53.3	251	59.3	300	56.6	349	57.9	398	57.2
7	54.3	56	51.5	105	56.4	154	59.6	203	53.8	252	53.6	301	58.9	350	60.6	399	59.4
8	58.5	57	55.5	106	56.8	155	56.1	204	56.3	253	57.6	302	59.9	351	62.1	400	50.6
9	56.5	58	55.9	107	50.3	156	57.4	205	54.9	254	56.8	303	58.8	352	59.5	401	51.8
10	59.6	59	59.0	108	54.4	157	53.1	206	54.5	255	57.2	304	55.3	353	62.8	402	56.2
11	54.5	60	55.6	109	55.0	158	55.8	207	55.8	256	58.8	305	55.8	354	61.3	403	53.6
12	53.3	61	56.7	110	55.0	159	61.3	208	58.9	257	55.3	306	55.9	355	62.3	404	56.5
13	55.8	62	59.8	111	56.4	160	60.3	209	63.1	258	64.5	307	57.8	356	56.9	405	54.2
14	53.5	63	57.5	112	53.3	161	57.5	210	55.7	259	58.0	308	58.4	357	58.9	406	56.1
15	52.4	64	56.5	113	53.2	162	52.3	211	52.8	260	56.8	309	55.7	358	63.3	407	60.0
16	55.4	65	54.3	114	54.7	163	59.4	212	52.8	261	58.1	310	54.5	359	62.0	408	53.2
17	58.2	66	52.8	115	55.6	164	57.3	213	56.4	262	58.6	311	57.2	360	60.2	409	53.7
18	56.4	67	57.8	116	54.6	165	54.1	214	59.0	263	62.6	312	51.6	361	59.7	410	53.5
19	55.3	68	54.0	117	62.0	166	50.8	215	59.1	264	59.8	313	53.2	362	62.0	411	57.8
20	56.9	69	56.1	118	57.4	167	50.3	216	53.3	265	60.2	314	58.1	363	56.1	412	58.4
21	56.3	70	49.7	119	57.3	168	53.2	217	54.9	266	59.4	315	56.4	364	58.1	413	59.8
22	54.1	71	59.9	120	60.0	169	55.9	218	60.6	267	62.9	316	56.1	365	55.3	414	59.6
23	53.5	72	60.1	121	58.4	170	60.5	219	55.8	268	63.4	317	54.3	366	52.0	415	56.5
24	59.5	73	58.8	122	60.3	171	60.1	220	56.4	269	58.9	318	56.5	367	51.2	416	59.7
25	58.5	74	57.9	123	60.5	172	52.0	221	56.4	270	59.8	319	53.0	368	53.7	417	60.5
26	59.6	75	59.1	124	55.5	173	53.2	222	56.8	271	61.0	320	54.8	369	56.2	418	60.0
27	56.8	76	59.9	125	55.1	174	57.2	223	56.8	272	63.8	321	58.4	370	55.9	419	52.7
28	55.9	77	63.7	126	52.7	175	52.0	224	57.6	273	59.8	322	60.6	371	58.1	420	51.9
29	56.7	78	57.9	127	52.1	176	53.3	225	52.5	274	59.4	323	55.0	372	60.7	421	57.4
30	56.9	79	61.0	128	56.1	177	52.7	226	57.4	275	56.5	324	58.4	373	58.3	422	53.5
31	59.8	80	54.6	129	57.6	178	55.7	227	56.4	276	59.1	325	63.5	374	54.6	423	54.2
32	60.4	81	59.0	130	51.4	179	58.3	228	57.6	277	60.0	326	56.4	375	50.4	424	49.8

Table A2—*Continued.*

Series C2 (N = 437)

33	55.3	82	52.4	131	53.0	180	57.9	229	58.6	278	56.9	327	60.6	376	52.2	425	51.0
34	58.7	83	56.0	132	52.5	181	53.7	230	56.8	279	57.9	328	60.1	377	53.3	426	47.8
35	51.6	84	59.9	133	56.6	182	56.9	231	57.2	280	59.4	329	60.0	378	63.3	427	53.8
36	56.9	85	60.0	134	56.4	183	57.4	232	59.7	281	58.9	330	56.0	379	61.4	428	50.7
37	50.1	86	55.4	135	59.4	184	53.4	233	58.8	282	51.3	331	56.2	380	62.8	429	52.6
38	51.6	87	60.3	136	57.3	185	57.3	234	52.3	283	55.0	332	62.7	381	59.3	430	61.4
39	53.6	88	54.9	137	57.6	186	54.0	235	57.8	284	56.7	333	57.2	382	57.9	431	53.5
40	58.7	89	57.8	138	59.8	187	58.0	236	55.9	285	53.4	334	57.5	383	66.7	432	58.6
41	52.1	90	58.2	139	57.8	188	53.8	237	55.1	286	52.9	335	61.7	384	64.6	433	55.8
42	52.7	91	57.6	140	62.8	189	53.0	238	55.7	287	53.8	336	54.9	385	58.0	434	58.8
43	55.7	92	55.9	141	55.1	190	54.3	239	54.7	288	54.2	337	57.3	386	61.8	435	60.5
44	59.2	93	55.1	142	59.8	191	51.7	240	57.5	289	56.6	338	59.4	387	60.4	436	57.2
45	59.3	94	56.4	143	57.9	192	55.3	241	58.4	290	55.0	339	58.3	388	52.5	437	57.1
46	55.1	95	58.5	144	56.3	193	56.1	242	60.3	291	56.5	340	58.0	389	51.7		
47	53.2	96	55.4	145	59.7	194	57.2	243	60.9	292	54.8	341	59.8	390	53.9		
48	56.0	97	55.5	146	54.5	195	58.3	244	55.3	293	57.4	342	57.3	391	53.2		
49	56.7	98	54.2	147	59.8	196	56.4	245	59.1	294	58.6	343	60.1	392	55.4		

Table A3

Series C3 (N = 536)

#		#		#		#		#		#		#		#		#	
1	48.5	61	51.3	121	49.1	181	48.4	241	48.9	301	53.3	361	51.4	421	54.9	481	56.4
2	53.2	62	49.6	122	46.2	182	49.4	242	50.0	302	51.7	362	52.3	422	52.0	482	54.7
3	50.2	63	49.3	123	49.7	183	48.3	243	48.6	303	53.1	363	50.3	423	51.2	483	52.6
4	49.5	64	51.4	124	46.5	184	49.9	244	50.1	304	52.4	364	48.6	424	55.8	484	52.1
5	52.9	65	47.7	125	47.9	185	51.3	245	52.5	305	53.6	365	53.8	425	53.6	485	55.0
6	51.2	66	48.4	126	47.8	186	51.5	246	50.1	306	52.2	366	50.8	426	55.4	486	55.8
7	49.1	67	51.0	127	50.5	187	48.9	247	52.6	307	54.5	367	53.4	427	55.8	487	53.9
8	52.8	68	49.5	128	49.5	188	49.2	248	53.1	308	53.5	368	53.9	428	56.4	488	56.0
9	49.9	69	50.2	129	50.9	189	52.4	249	52.2	309	53.3	369	53.8	429	55.6	489	54.9
10	50.2	70	46.2	130	49.1	190	48.6	250	51.8	310	54.1	370	52.6	430	53.6	490	54.8
11	52.0	71	50.0	131	47.4	191	52.6	251	52.1	311	57.1	371	54.1	431	55.9	491	53.8
12	52.0	72	48.0	132	48.6	192	48.9	252	51.0	312	52.5	372	53.0	432	55.0	492	53.3
13	49.5	73	48.4	133	51.8	193	50.4	253	54.5	313	53.3	373	53.9	433	55.9	493	58.3
14	47.2	74	51.5	134	48.7	194	48.0	254	56.3	314	55.5	374	54.4	434	55.7	494	57.2
15	49.5	75	50.8	135	47.7	195	49.5	255	54.4	315	56.4	375	54.9	435	56.3	495	55.8
16	48.0	76	52.9	136	47.4	196	49.4	256	54.0	316	54.1	376	54.0	436	56.0	496	57.8
17	50.1	77	49.4	137	47.5	197	49.0	257	56.1	317	53.0	377	55.3	437	53.9	497	58.8
18	49.8	78	51.6	138	51.7	198	48.1	258	54.2	318	55.3	378	52.3	438	56.2	498	54.0
19	48.4	79	55.4	139	50.7	199	49.7	259	54.0	319	54.1	379	53.7	439	56.7	499	54.0
20	49.8	80	49.7	140	48.9	200	48.6	260	53.1	320	54.7	380	50.9	440	56.0	500	54.6
21	49.0	81	49.0	141	50.7	201	48.2	261	54.1	321	53.1	381	54.1	441	54.2	501	53.8
22	51.2	82	52.2	142	50.3	202	48.4	262	53.5	322	52.9	382	53.9	442	51.6	502	58.9
23	49.5	83	51.7	143	49.6	203	53.1	263	56.1	323	54.3	383	53.6	443	56.0	503	55.8
24	49.0	84	49.0	144	47.0	204	48.1	264	53.2	324	55.7	384	53.5	444	54.1	504	58.6
25	48.4	85	51.3	145	48.3	205	49.9	265	53.6	325	51.3	385	53.5	445	56.8	505	53.0
26	48.3	86	49.4	146	47.1	206	49.3	266	53.5	326	52.1	386	52.6	446	50.4	506	58.5
27	50.0	87	50.1	147	48.5	207	48.3	267	54.5	327	51.3	387	52.8	447	57.4	507	56.1
28	49.3	88	51.9	148	47.9	208	51.8	268	52.7	328	54.1	388	52.3	448	52.9	508	54.0
29	51.5	89	49.1	149	50.8	209	49.5	269	53.6	329	50.2	389	53.9	449	57.5	509	52.5
30	51.2	90	49.6	150	49.3	210	49.1	270	53.1	330	52.6	390	54.5	450	57.9	510	54.2
31	49.6	91	49.3	151	52.4	211	48.0	271	53.2	331	54.2	391	55.1	451	54.3	511	52.3
32	52.6	92	49.1	152	51.8	212	49.5	272	53.6	332	51.4	392	54.2	452	58.6	512	54.5

Table A3—*Continued.*

Series C3 (N = 536)

33	55.5	93	49.7	153	53.1	213	51.5	273	54.9	333	54.4	393	54.2	453	58.0	513	56.9
34	49.6	94	48.5	154	51.1	214	48.7	274	53.9	334	53.9	394	52.7	454	55.9	514	54.9
35	52.2	95	48.2	155	52.8	215	48.1	275	52.1	335	50.9	395	53.0	455	55.4	515	52.9
36	54.0	96	48.6	156	51.2	216	49.9	276	54.9	336	54.5	396	55.0	456	57.0	516	54.0
37	49.5	97	49.2	157	51.9	217	51.2	277	54.7	337	50.8	397	53.1	457	56.4	517	53.4
38	51.0	98	48.9	158	50.8	218	49.3	278	52.9	338	52.5	398	51.6	458	56.2	518	51.6
39	49.7	99	50.4	159	51.5	219	49.5	279	52.7	339	51.4	399	52.9	459	55.0	519	50.7
40	49.9	100	48.7	160	51.5	220	47.3	280	54.7	340	49.5	400	53.3	460	54.9	520	52.5
41	50.0	101	49.2	161	53.2	221	52.1	281	53.5	341	54.3	401	50.8	461	55.6	521	52.3
42	50.7	102	49.0	162	51.5	222	51.3	282	56.7	342	53.2	402	50.2	462	55.9	522	52.8
43	49.5	103	48.0	163	52.0	223	52.1	283	53.3	343	50.2	403	51.0	463	54.8	523	53.7
44	51.0	104	47.4	164	53.8	224	50.1	284	51.7	344	48.2	404	52.1	464	53.4	524	50.9
45	53.9	105	48.3	165	54.3	225	48.7	285	55.0	345	50.5	405	50.7	465	53.2	525	54.1
46	49.1	106	47.3	166	51.0	226	47.9	286	53.5	346	51.5	406	52.8	466	57.6	526	53.8
47	50.9	107	48.9	167	52.8	227	49.2	287	54.3	347	53.8	407	50.2	467	53.1	527	51.1
48	51.2	108	47.8	168	51.0	228	47.4	288	56.2	348	50.2	408	51.6	468	53.3	528	52.0
49	51.5	109	49.7	169	52.6	229	49.3	289	57.3	349	50.9	409	52.3	469	54.2	529	53.5
50	51.7	110	48.3	170	54.5	230	50.3	290	53.0	350	50.4	410	52.2	470	53.5	530	55.3
51	52.4	111	48.3	171	53.5	231	49.4	291	55.5	351	51.7	411	51.6	471	55.5	531	51.7
52	48.0	112	47.2	172	51.5	232	49.2	292	54.1	352	52.9	412	53.7	472	57.0	532	54.7
53	52.3	113	48.5	173	50.3	233	49.2	293	52.6	353	48.9	413	51.1	473	53.4	533	55.4
54	51.7	114	50.5	174	51.6	234	48.6	294	56.0	354	51.8	414	52.9	474	54.2	534	56.3
55	50.3	115	50.6	175	51.3	235	48.2	295	53.5	355	53.9	415	55.7	475	53.0	535	54.0
56	53.0	116	50.0	176	50.7	236	51.5	296	52.2	356	51.9	416	53.5	476	54.6	536	53.1
57	49.6	117	46.2	177	51.6	237	51.9	297	52.9	357	48.1	417	54.5	477	53.9		
58	49.1	118	51.8	178	48.9	238	49.3	298	52.1	358	50.3	418	54.1	478	57.9		
59	50.5	119	48.3	179	50.5	239	49.4	299	52.6	359	53.6	419	52.2	479	53.1		
60	51.1	120	47.9	180	50.2	240	49.5	300	50.3	360	53.5	420	54.0	480	54.8		

Table A4

Series C4 (N = 402)

1	44.5	46	57.9	91	46.3	136	44.1	181	51.3	226	47.8	271	49.3	316	49.6	361	45.1
2	48.7	47	57.1	92	46.3	137	47.4	182	51.0	227	42.5	272	44.7	317	44.3	362	46.8
3	47.4	48	49.0	93	48.9	138	45.3	183	43.8	228	43.9	273	46.1	318	49.5	363	42.6
4	50.1	49	54.0	94	42.8	139	45.5	184	48.9	229	40.4	274	46.1	319	42.0	364	46.2
5	48.9	50	51.6	95	46.6	140	44.3	185	48.6	230	42.2	275	43.8	320	46.1	365	47.1
6	48.7	51	51.2	96	40.8	141	42.7	186	42.7	231	47.1	276	45.8	321	44.2	366	43.9
7	49.3	52	48.5	97	42.0	142	46.4	187	44.2	232	48.5	277	52.1	322	42.6	367	45.5
8	44.1	53	49.4	98	41.8	143	46.5	188	44.2	233	49.5	278	49.2	323	42.7	368	44.6
9	48.2	54	53.8	99	42.5	144	44.2	189	43.5	234	45.5	279	50.5	324	46.1	369	46.4
10	46.9	55	47.1	100	47.5	145	47.5	190	42.6	235	44.5	280	51.7	325	44.3	370	48.2
11	46.1	56	59.6	101	46.9	146	49.0	191	45.5	236	47.8	281	50.9	326	45.2	371	44.8
12	46.1	57	52.4	102	43.9	147	47.0	192	46.5	237	46.5	282	51.3	327	49.8	372	47.3
13	40.5	58	44.0	103	48.0	148	49.7	193	48.2	238	45.4	283	44.2	328	42.0	373	43.0
14	45.0	59	54.2	104	50.5	149	54.7	194	48.4	239	49.5	284	51.0	329	45.6	374	42.6
15	49.5	60	50.0	105	47.3	150	54.3	195	43.7	240	51.5	285	43.8	330	47.7	375	44.5
16	41.0	61	52.7	106	48.4	151	50.3	196	45.5	241	45.2	286	48.9	331	45.9	376	44.0
17	49.1	62	51.6	107	50.4	152	49.8	197	45.5	242	46.9	287	48.6	332	47.9	377	45.4
18	51.0	63	56.5	108	44.7	153	53.3	198	43.9	243	50.9	288	42.6	333	47.6	378	41.9
19	45.8	64	54.1	109	40.9	154	51.1	199	48.8	244	51.9	289	44.2	334	48.3	379	46.4
20	47.5	65	59.0	110	46.5	155	46.1	200	47.8	245	46.3	290	43.8	335	47.4	380	42.5
21	52.0	66	58.9	111	48.3	156	51.5	201	43.7	246	46.2	291	43.6	336	47.2	381	46.4
22	51.5	67	53.0	112	47.4	157	45.3	202	43.4	247	45.1	292	42.6	337	46.9	382	51.0
23	48.4	68	47.4	113	41.0	158	45.5	203	47.0	248	50.9	293	45.5	338	46.4	383	50.0
24	51.7	69	48.6	114	44.4	159	43.2	204	45.1	249	47.9	294	46.5	339	44.3	384	46.5
25	47.1	70	50.6	115	44.1	160	47.6	205	46.9	250	46.4	295	48.2	340	45.8	385	48.9
26	46.2	71	52.2	116	41.5	161	47.4	206	46.2	251	50.7	296	48.4	341	43.4	386	49.2
27	43.4	72	45.6	117	45.8	162	51.0	207	45.3	252	48.9	297	45.5	342	44.1	387	45.8
28	46.8	73	54.0	118	44.0	163	51.8	208	48.3	253	46.7	298	43.9	343	46.4	388	47.6
29	53.4	74	52.8	119	47.7	164	49.9	209	46.0	254	44.8	299	48.8	344	48.3	389	41.8
30	50.4	75	50.8	120	45.1	165	49.4	210	45.6	255	43.0	300	47.5	345	44.7	390	46.0
31	55.9	76	49.8	121	44.7	166	47.8	211	48.3	256	43.5	301	52.0	346	46.5	391	49.5
32	51.7	77	47.9	122	41.1	167	48.7	212	49.2	257	45.8	302	50.2	347	54.0	392	42.4

Table A4—*Continued.*

Series C4 (N = 402)

33	54.5	78	52.2	123	43.2	168	47.4	213	45.1	258	41.1	303	42.6	348	46.1	393	47.3
34	48.4	79	47.9	124	42.7	169	48.0	214	44.5	259	45.8	304	52.1	349	45.2	394	49.0
35	53.3	80	46.3	125	40.6	170	49.8	215	43.5	260	44.5	305	46.6	350	56.5	395	46.1
36	44.9	81	50.4	126	44.8	171	47.5	216	45.7	261	47.0	306	48.0	351	48.5	396	56.0
37	52.3	82	48.3	127	47.8	172	46.5	217	43.7	262	43.5	307	43.4	352	51.0	397	51.0
38	51.7	83	48.1	128	48.2	173	46.0	218	42.5	263	44.0	308	42.5	353	48.3	398	47.0
39	49.3	84	47.5	129	51.4	174	45.9	219	44.3	264	45.7	309	47.6	354	47.5	399	47.8
40	45.1	85	56.5	130	47.4	175	52.1	220	44.8	265	47.5	310	48.4	355	44.5	400	45.5
41	50.8	86	51.2	131	49.7	176	49.2	221	44.5	266	42.4	311	45.2	356	52.0	401	50.6
42	45.3	87	45.3	132	48.3	177	50.5	222	46.1	267	45.4	312	48.7	357	53.5	402	51.2
43	53.7	88	49.2	133	51.8	178	51.7	223	45.6	268	50.4	313	49.0	358	44.9		
44	51.3	89	50.5	134	44.8	179	50.9	224	42.6	269	51.9	314	52.2	359	46.5		
45	58.1	90	44.6	135	50.6	180	48.1	225	43.1	270	50.8	315	49.1	360	45.2		

Table A5

Series C4' (N = 402)

1	28.5	46	32.7	91	28.0	136	28.0	181	30.1	226	25.8	271	32.0	316	27.2	361	32.0
2	28.0	47	37.0	92	28.8	137	29.8	182	23.5	227	23.8	272	27.5	317	22.4	362	27.5
3	25.8	48	28.2	93	29.6	138	29.5	183	25.5	228	24.7	273	27.4	318	31.2	363	26.2
4	27.0	49	29.4	94	26.6	139	29.2	184	32.2	229	23.9	274	28.1	319	28.2	364	27.5
5	27.5	50	31.5	95	28.2	140	23.8	185	30.7	230	24.1	275	28.0	320	23.5	365	30.0
6	28.7	51	28.2	96	22.1	141	24.0	186	24.9	231	25.7	276	26.7	321	24.4	366	25.4
7	27.3	52	30.8	97	25.3	142	26.9	187	28.0	232	26.3	277	31.5	322	26.5	367	28.2
8	23.8	53	29.6	98	22.8	143	27.0	188	25.0	233	28.4	278	31.1	323	30.7	368	29.0
9	28.5	54	32.5	99	26.8	144	26.5	189	26.0	234	28.8	279	31.0	324	22.1	369	30.2
10	26.2	55	29.7	100	25.4	145	26.9	190	26.1	235	26.5	280	31.1	325	22.4	370	25.8
11	28.1	56	37.2	101	26.3	146	30.4	191	22.1	236	28.9	281	32.6	326	23.0	371	24.0
12	27.1	57	32.1	102	26.5	147	28.5	192	24.0	237	27.0	282	32.7	327	29.0	372	31.0
13	21.2	58	20.6	103	29.3	148	31.8	193	26.1	238	28.2	283	25.4	328	21.8	373	23.9
14	25.0	59	34.1	104	26.9	149	32.6	194	26.0	239	31.1	284	23.5	329	27.1	374	23.8
15	28.6	60	29.7	105	25.7	150	34.7	195	21.2	240	31.7	285	25.5	330	27.4	375	28.0
16	20.9	61	33.1	106	28.8	151	31.0	196	23.1	241	26.0	286	32.2	331	26.2	376	28.7
17	27.5	62	29.2	107	30.6	152	33.7	197	24.7	242	24.7	287	30.7	332	28.9	377	29.5
18	31.7	63	33.5	108	25.7	153	34.0	198	25.3	243	33.5	288	24.0	333	27.6	378	24.3
19	25.9	64	29.0	109	21.2	154	36.2	199	28.0	244	34.5	289	28.0	334	29.1	379	30.6
20	27.6	65	36.9	110	30.3	155	29.8	200	26.5	245	27.0	290	23.2	335	29.0	380	25.4
21	34.0	66	37.0	111	29.1	156	34.1	201	27.7	246	31.5	291	26.0	336	30.0	381	29.0
22	32.6	67	30.5	112	28.4	157	26.3	202	23.8	247	26.7	292	21.0	337	28.2	382	33.0
23	30.3	68	25.8	113	24.1	158	29.5	203	28.5	248	30.5	293	19.0	338	27.0	383	32.9
24	31.8	69	30.7	114	25.1	159	21.2	204	25.3	249	28.7	294	23.0	339	24.0	384	28.0
25	27.6	70	33.9	115	24.7	160	30.8	205	26.2	250	29.6	295	23.0	340	25.2	385	33.0
26	29.1	71	33.1	116	25.0	161	30.6	206	25.9	251	24.5	296	23.1	341	23.9	386	28.0
27	27.2	72	27.3	117	25.7	162	34.3	207	27.8	252	31.1	297	19.1	342	24.9	387	27.9
28	27.4	73	32.4	118	26.0	163	35.7	208	27.3	253	30.4	298	21.3	343	26.5	388	36.1
29	35.4	74	32.7	119	27.9	164	30.0	209	28.2	254	30.1	299	24.0	344	30.1	389	27.2
30	32.2	75	31.9	120	25.1	165	31.7	210	27.1	255	26.3	300	23.5	345	26.4	390	30.2
31	34.1	76	27.9	121	25.4	166	32.3	211	27.3	256	23.6	301	35.8	346	29.2	391	30.9
32	32.0	77	29.1	122	22.7	167	29.7	212	28.6	257	28.8	302	31.1	347	34.1	392	26.7

Table A5—*Continued.*

Series C4' (N = 402)

33	32.9	78	34.6	123	24.0	168	30.7	213	26.5	258	26.1	303	25.0	348	31.8	393	29.7
34	30.6	79	26.7	124	23.3	169	31.2	214	25.5	259	28.2	304	30.1	349	29.4	394	32.0
35	35.1	80	25.9	125	19.7	170	32.6	215	25.0	260	27.5	305	25.5	350	32.3	395	31.2
36	24.9	81	30.8	126	24.2	171	31.5	216	26.3	261	30.7	306	26.0	351	30.9	396	26.9
37	32.9	82	28.8	127	30.0	172	29.4	217	24.7	262	27.3	307	24.3	352	30.0	397	25.3
38	34.5	83	28.1	128	29.5	173	28.7	218	25.1	263	24.6	308	26.5	353	33.5	398	30.8
39	32.2	84	28.7	129	29.3	174	28.8	219	24.0	264	26.5	309	26.1	354	30.2	399	31.1
40	30.5	85	32.9	130	29.2	175	31.5	220	26.5	265	32.6	310	27.0	355	28.7	400	34.1
41	30.7	86	32.2	131	30.5	176	31.1	221	27.3	266	26.4	311	27.3	356	29.7	401	34.0
42	29.1	87	29.3	132	29.7	177	31.0	222	26.7	267	24.5	312	30.5	357	32.6	402	31.5
43	36.3	88	32.3	133	27.9	178	31.1	223	25.7	268	28.9	313	28.0	358	28.1		
44	35.1	89	32.2	134	26.0	179	32.6	224	24.5	269	32.0	314	30.5	359	26.3		
45	34.2	90	29.9	135	34.6	180	26.6	225	26.0	270	32.6	315	29.0	360	26.1		

References

[1] Von Neumann, J., Kent, R., Bellison, H., and Hart, B., "The Mean Square Successive Difference," *Annals of Mathematical Statistics*, Vol. 12, 1941, pp. 153–162.
[2] Hart, B., "Significance Levels for the Ratio of the Mean Square Successive Difference to the Variance," *Annals of Mathematical Statistics*, Vol. 13, 1942, pp. 445–447.
[3] Hald, D., "Statistical Theory with Engineering Applications," Wiley, New York, 1952, p. 357.
[4] Taerwe, L., "Aspects of the Stochastic Nature of Concrete Strength Including Compliance Control," Doctoral Thesis, Ghent, Belgium, 1985 (in Dutch).
[5] Kendall, M. and Stuart, A., *The Advanced Theory of Statistics*, Vol. 2, Griffin, London, 1979.

H. C. Visvesvaraya[1] and Ajoy K. Mullick[2]

Quality of Cements in India—Results of Three Decadal Surveys

REFERENCE: Visvesvaraya, H. C. and Mullick, A. K., **"Quality of Cements in India—Results of Three Decadal Surveys,"** *Uniformity of Cement Strength, ASTM STP 961,* E. Farkas and P. Klieger, Eds., American Society for Testing and Materials, Philadelphia, 1987, pp. 66–79.

ABSTRACT: Increases in cement production in India over the years have been achieved with due considerations to the quality requirements. Systematic data on the quality characteristics of the cement produced in the last three decades indicate the compressive strength of cements to exceed the minimum requirements with sufficient margins. The overall coefficient of variation on the entire production from different plants has remained steady at a level of about 18%. The in-plant coefficient of variation ranges from 4 to 19%.

KEY WORDS: cement plants, cements, coal, compressive strength, fineness, India, portland cements, portland pozzolana cements, portland slag cements, quality, raw materials, specifications, surveys, tests, variation

The first cement plant in India, in the year 1914, had an annual production of about 1000 tonnes; the installed capacity in India by the end of March 1986 was 44 million tonnes with production during the year 1985–86 of the order of 33 million tonnes. The installed capacity at the end of the 7th Five Year Plan (1989–90) has been planned at 62 million tonnes and by the year 2000 A.D. may exceed 100 million tonnes. To be found in the heterogeneous cement industry in India are: (1) large plants having a capacity of a million tonnes per year in single line, (2) medium size plants having capacities close to half-a-million tonnes per year in a single or multi-lines, as well as (3) miniplants having capacities less than 66 000 tonnes per year in single or multilines. About 35% of the present production of cement comes from wet process plants.

Apart from the growth in production, the other discernable technological changes in the cement scene over the decades have been: (1) in the product mix; (2) adoption of dry process technology with preheaters and precalcinators, especially in large size plants that have come up lately; and (3) conversion of existing plants from wet to semidry/dry processes. Although Indian Standards Institution (ISI) specifications cover a number of types of cements, the main production is of three types: ordinary portland cement (OPC), portland pozzolana cement (PPC), and portland slag cement (PSC). The relative proportion of different types of cement produced in the country is indicated in Table 1. Special cements like high-strength cements, white cement, oil-well cement, etc., are categorized under "Others" in Table 1. From the late seventies the relative proportion of blended cements has gone up and presently comprises nearly 70% of the total production—57% as PPC and another 14% as PSC.

It its pursuit of growth, the cement industry in India faces the constraints of raw materials and fuels, apart from demands of national priorities, for example, energy conservation, environmental improvement, and increasing productivity. While sufficient deposits of limestone are available in the country—estimated at over 80 000 million tonnes, there are inherent problems

[1]Chairman and director-general, National Council for Cement and Building Materials, New Delhi, India.
[2]Joint director, National Council for Cement and Building Materials, New Delhi, India.

TABLE 1—*Production of different varieties of cements—1973 to 1985 (in million tonnes).*

Year	OPC	PPC	PSC	Other Varieties	Total
1973	13.05	0.05	1.84	0.05	14.99
1974	11.70	0.49	1.84	0.30	14.33
1975	12.05	0.86	2.30	1.13	16.34
1976	14.63	0.75	3.19	0.13	18.70
1977	13.67	1.96	3.28	0.25	19.16
1978	10.31	6.06	3.08	0.16	19.61
1979	8.35	6.66	3.16	0.16	18.39
1980	6.28	8.37	3.08	0.16	17.89
1981	4.86	12.29	3.47	0.24	20.86
1982	4.97	13.45	3.93	0.24	22.59
1983	6.80	14.46	3.99	0.17	25.42
1984	8.17	16.69	4.08	0.21	29.15
1985 (up to September)	8.73	10.82	3.29	0.15	22.99

in the complexities of their geological formations as well as the problem of marginal quality. The Indian cement industry is required to use fuel in the form of coal of very high ash content and low colorific value, which is seldom used by cement industries in other parts of the world.

On the face of such severe constraints, the cements produced in the country have to conform to national standards which are generally at par with international standards [1]. There is constant monitoring of the quality of cement by the National Council of Cement and Building Materials (NCB) and others.

This paper summarizes the results of periodic surveys of the quality of the entire production of cements in India over the last three decades, with specific reference to compressive strength characteristics. All the samples were collected from the cement plants. Trend analysis is presented in terms of the raw materials, fuels, process technologies, and the total production capacity. The resultant impact on standardization activities and concrete technology practices is discussed.

Results of Periodic Surveys

The Sixties

The first comprehensive survey of the quality of cement in India was reported in 1968 [2]. The total production of cement at that time was around 12 million tonnes. The investigations were initiated with the basic objectives of: (1) arriving at a revised gradation of the standard sand to be used for testing the cement in mortars; (2) determining the optimum quantity of gauging water to be used in preparing specimens to ensure full compaction, highest reproducibility, and strength without any bleeding or honeycombing taking place; and, following these, (3) fixing the revised values of minimum compressive strengths to be specified in the IS specifications as a result of changeover from single-sized standard sand to regraded sand. Ever since the completion of these investigations, the testing of cement per Indian standard specification (IS: 4031–1968) envisages use of graded standard sand having three equal size fractions of coarse (2 mm to 1 mm), medium (1 mm to 500 μm) and fine (500 μm—downwards) and the water content in 1:3 mortar equalling $(P/4 + 3)$ percent of the total mass, where P is the water requirement for normal consistency. On an average, the water requirement for normal consistency of Indian cements is around 28%. This corresponds to a water-cement (W-C) ratio of approximately 0.4

in the mortar mixes. All the compressive strength results presented in this paper are on this basis of testing on 7.07-cm-size cube specimens having an area of face equal to 50 cm².

Random samples of OPC from 37 cement plants using both the previous procedure (with single-sized standard sand) and the revised procedure (with regraded standard sand) were tested. A summary of compressive strength of cements at 3, 7, and 28 days tested in one control laboratory are given in Table 2. The overall coefficient of variation was of the order of 17 to 18%. All the cement samples satisfied revised requirements of minimum compressive strength stipulated in the Standard, that is, 16 MPa at three days and 22 MPa at seven days.

The Seventies

The next comprehensive investigation was taken up during 1976-77, when the total cement production in the country was around 19 million tonnes [3]. Weekly samples of OPC from 39 cement plants for 58 weeks of production were tested for physical properties and chemical composition. These tests were aimed at fixing a 28-day compressive strength limit for OPC and also for strength grading of cements. Availability of weekly samples enabled a measure of in-plant variability.

An overall summary of results on tests for physical characteristics are given in Table 3. Figures 1, 2, and 3 give histograms of compressive strengths at ages 3, 7, and 28 days, respectively.

In so far as results of tests on weekly samples from any particular plant are concerned, Figs. 4 and 5 reflect the general trend. The in-plant coefficient of variation in compressive strengths of weekly samples ranged from 4.2 to 18.9% and was not constant for different test ages from a particular plant. Nearly 38% of test results showed less than 8% coefficient of variation in 28-day compressive strengths.

In view of the fact that a construction site may receive cement from more than one plant, consideration of overall variability was also important. The overall coefficient of variation of

TABLE 2—*Statistical analysis of compressive strengths (in MPa) of cements (1968).*

Age, Days	Number of Samples	Max	Min	Avg	Standard Deviation	Coefficient of Variation, %
3	37	35.2	16.1	25.7	4.8	18.7
7	37	43.8	18.0	32.3	5.8	18.0
28	37	55.6	25.8	43.9	7.6	17.3

TABLE 3—*Statistical analysis of physical characteristics of cements (1976-77).*

Characteristics	No. of Samples	Max	Min	Avg	Standard Deviation	Coefficient of Variation, %
Compressive strength, MPa						
3 day	402	44.3	14.3	26.3	5.0	19.0
7 day	281	59.7	21.7	36.1	6.4	17.7
28 day	507	75.7	31.2	50.5	7.5	14.8
Fineness (Blaine), m²/kg	505	463	227	314	36.8	11.7
Setting time, min						
Initial	499	215	30	86.0	36.0	41.8
Final	499	420	60	235.5	63.7	27.0
Water content for normal consistency						
(P), %	507	34	23.4	27.8	1.4	5.1

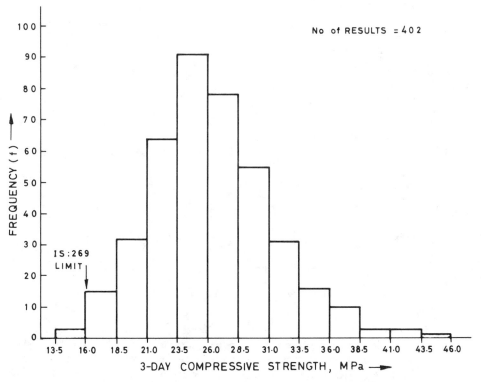

FIG. 1—*Histogram of the 3-day strength of cement samples (1976–77).*

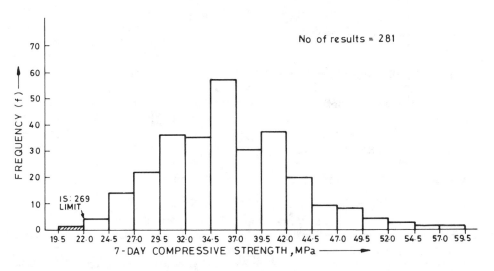

FIG. 2—*Histogram of the 7-day strength of cement samples (1976–77).*

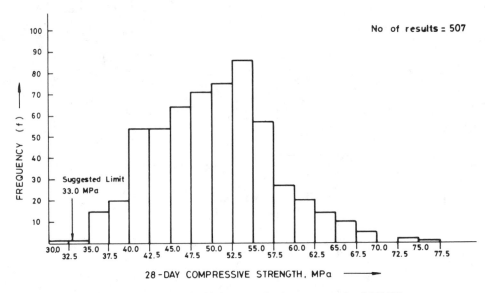

FIG. 3—*Histogram of the 28-day strength of cement samples (1976–77).*

compressive strength of all cement samples was of the order of 18%, that is, the same as in the previous survey. The average fineness of all the cement samples was 314 kg/m² (Blaine). The coefficient of variation of fineness was 11.7%, while for setting times were 41.8 (initial) and 27.0% (final), indicating greater control on grinding, which is more energy-consuming, and lesser control on setting times than on compressive strength. Greater variability in setting times and compressive strengths are indicative of variability in composition of raw meal, apart from variations in the pyroprocessing and finish grinding, which were expected to be better controlled. The average ash content in coal used as fuel was reported to be 20 to 28%.

The average lime-saturation factor (LSF) expressed as

$$\frac{\%\,CaO - 0.7 \times \%\,SO_3}{2.8 \times \%\,SiO_2 + 1.2 \times \%\,Al_2O_3 + 0.65 \times \%\,Fe_2O_3}$$

was 0.90.

The total alkalies varied from 0.2 to 1.2%, with nearly 40% of the results being 0.6% or below (Fig. 6).

Almost all the cement samples met the specification limits of compressive strength with margins larger than the previous survey. On statistical analysis of results, the 28-day strength limit of OPC was set at 33 MPa; in addition, two higher grades of OPC (with 28-day strengths of 43 and 53 MPa) were suggested. Average quality in the case of 38% of the plants was in excess of the highest grade contemplated.

Contemporary Situation

The cement scene in the eighties is characterized by many technological changes with depletion of reserves of good quality limestone within economic distances. Many old cement plants had to use marginal grade raw materials, and use of mineralizers and sweeteners had to be resorted to. The coal available as fuel is of poorer quality, with ash content up to 35 to 40%. This led to difficulties of proper burning as well as ash absorption in the clinker. While a con-

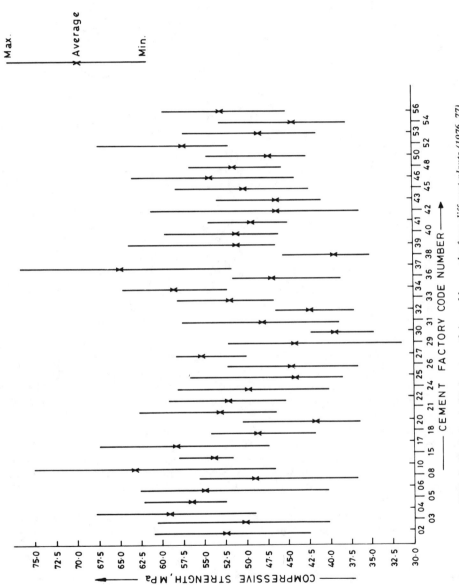

FIG. 4—*Variation in 28-day strength in weekly samples from different plants (1976–77).*

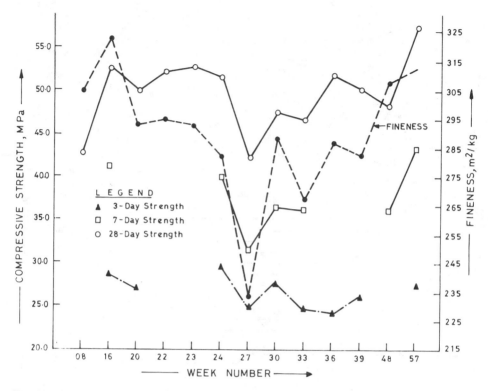

FIG. 5—*Weekly variation in fineness and compressive strength of cement from a typical plant (1976–77).*

siderable increase in production capacity as well as the number of plants is expected to increase the variability in the overall context, most of the large-sized newer plants with automated process control instrumentation were producing cements with stricter quality control. The most significant change, however, is the substantial production of blended cements, that is, PPC and PSC.

Ever since 1980 NCB has carried out surprise checks on the quality of cements from the plants on behalf of the Government. In addition, introduction of ISI Certification Mark Scheme on a compulsory basis since 1983 necessitated testing at NCB of cement samples from the plants collected by the regulatory agency. As a result, random samples of OPC as well as blended cements from almost all the existing 78 cement plants in the country have been periodically tested at NCB.

Results of tests of such samples comprise the contemporary survey which enables a comparative evaluation of strength characteristics of blended cements with OPC for the first time.

An overall summary of results on tests for compressive strength of different types of cements is given in Table 4.

Figures 7, 8 and 9 present a histogram of compressive strengths at different ages for the three types of cement. In spite of an increase in the number of plants from which these samples are drawn and the longer period over which the samples were collected, the overall variability in the compressive strength is found to be of the same order of magnitude as in the earlier surveys, indicative of better process and quality control. In so far as the OPC samples are concerned, the average of compressive strengths of all samples tested was similar to previous decades. However, when all types of cement samples are taken together, the overall average is found to be

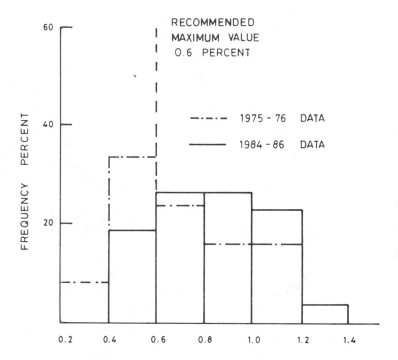

FIG. 6—*Distribution of total alkali content in cement samples.*

TABLE 4—*Statistical analysis of physical characteristics of cements (1980–86).*

| Type of Cement | Compressive Strength | | | | | | Fineness (Blaine) | |
| | Average MPa at Ages | | | Coefficient of Variation, % | | | Average, m²/kg | Coefficient of Variation, % |
	3 days	7 days	28 days	3 days	7 days	28 days		
OPC, PPC, PSC	25.6(214)[a]	34.3(475)	47.5(318)	22.6	18.7	18.0	362(475)	14.8
OPC only	26.4(154)	36.3(154)	53.0(57)	22.8	17.0	16.0	321(154)	13.1
PPC only	. . .	32.9(261)	46.3(261)	. . .	19.4	17.1	386(261)	11.6
PSC only	23.7(60)	35.0(60)	. . .	20.3	15.6	. . .	364(60)	14.0

[a]Figures in parentheses represent the number of samples.

lower. The blended cements (PPC and PSC) have, in general, about 10% lower strength than OPC samples from the same clinker [4]. Most would, however, have met the requirements of high-strength OPC if they did not contain pozzolana or slags. This is perhaps due to the fact that clinkers used in the manufacture of blended cements are carefully chosen and the percentage of additions are lower than the maximum limit prescribed. Data on high-strength and special grade high-strength cements manufactured were not separately available. However, nearly 35% of the total production conformed to the requirements of high-grade cements.

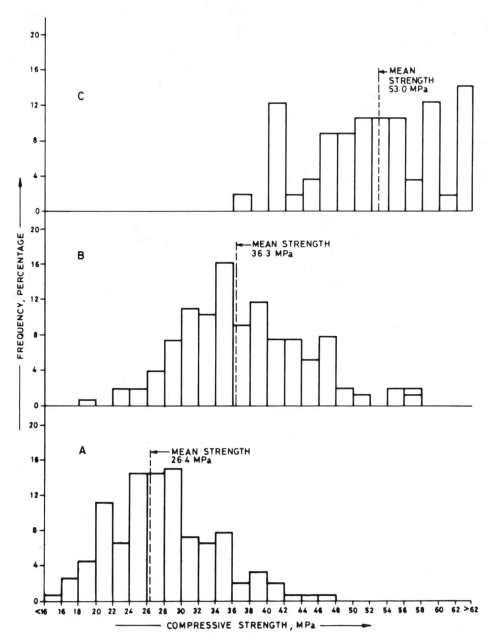

FIG. 7—*Histogram of compressive strength of OPC samples at different ages (1980–86): A = 3 days, B = 7 days, and C = 28 days.*

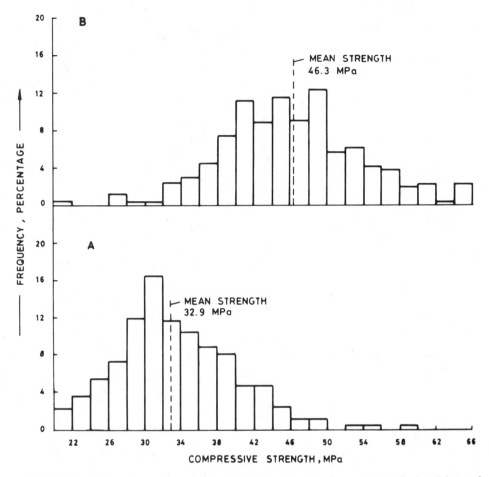

FIG. 8—*Histogram of compressive strength of PPC samples at different ages (1980–86). A = 7 days and B = 28 days.*

The average fineness of all cements was 362 m²/kg Blaine, which was higher than in the previous survey. This was mainly due to a larger share of blended cements which are required to be ground finer.

The alkali content in cement is shown in Fig. 6. Dry process plants resulted in higher alkali content, as expected, than in wet process plants. Significantly, cement plants of vertical shaft kiln (CRI-VSK) type resulted in lower alkali contents than in rotary kilns.

Impact on Concrete Technology

Concrete Mix Proportions

In view of the level of variability of strength characteristics of cements from the plants as well as the fact that a construction project may receive cement from different plants from time to time, adjustments in the concrete mix proportions to take into account variations in strength characteristics of cement become necessary in order to maintain the overall coefficient of varia-

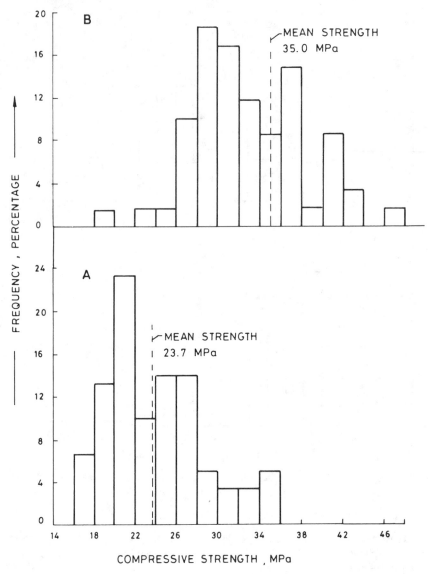

FIG. 9—*Histogram of compressive strength of PSC samples at different ages (1980–86). A = 3 days and B = 7 days.*

tion in the compressive strength of concrete within permissible limits. This can be accomplished by considering a series of strength-W-C relationships of the nature of Fig. 10 in concrete mix proportioning rather than a single generalized relationship. This would, however, necessitate the testing of the compressive strength of cement before trials for mix proportioning can be taken up and the total time required in trials is considerably increased. A method has, therefore, been evolved in NCB to take into account such variability in the quality of cement by means of accelerated strength testing [5]. In this procedure, cement is tested in a reference

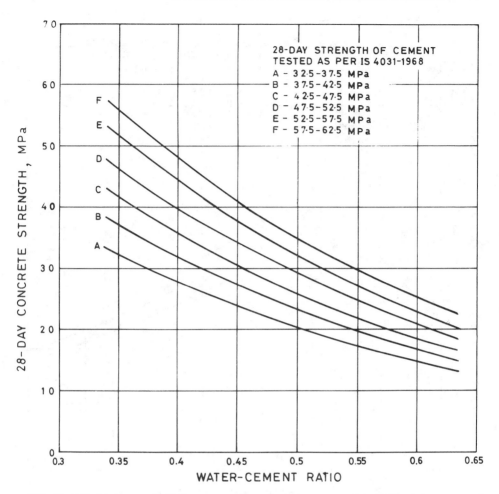

FIG. 10—*Relation between the 28-day compressive strength of concrete and the W-C ratio for cements of different 28-day strength.*

concrete mix rather than in standard mortar mixes, and its accelerated strength following a "boiling water" cycle of 28½ h is determined. An appropriate W/C ratio for the design strength is chosen from a relationship based on such an accelerated strength of cements (Fig. 11). Trial mixes are also verified through accelerated strength tests. Thus the concrete mix proportioning takes only three days. The method is incorporated in IS: 10262 for concrete mix design and is being successfully adopted.

Alkali Aggregate Reactions

The naturally occurring concrete aggregates in India were earlier believed to be innocuous. However, recent instances of distress to concrete dams built more than 25 years ago have now been related to alkali-silica reactions [6]. Apart from aggregates containing cryptocrystalline silica, for example, cherts and chalcedony, aggregates belonging compositionally to the granite-

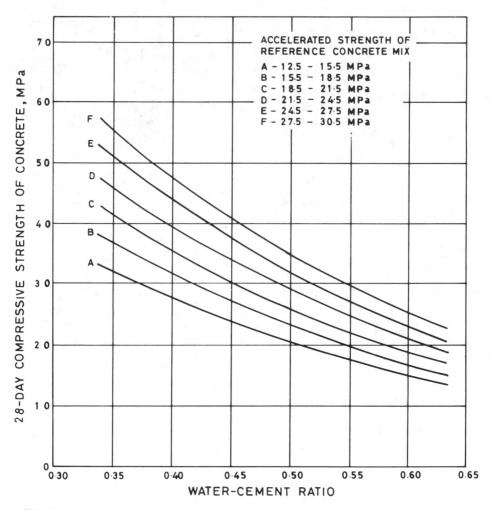

FIG. 11—*Relation between the 28-day compressive strength of concrete and the W-C ratio for cement having different strengths (accelerated test).*

granodiorite or granite-porphyry group with alkali feldspar and mica-bearing phases containing "strained" quartz with undulose extinction are also encountered. As a result, many of the mass concrete constructions to be taken up now require low-alkali cements.

As per data shown in Fig. 6, availability of low-alkali OPC is presently somewhat restricted. Cement substitutes like active pozzolana or slags are known to be useful in alleviating alkali-silica reaction, but the level of cement substitution has to be relatively high, for example, around 25 to 30%, when fly ash or calcined clay pozzolana are used and greater when slag is used (around 60%). In the context of the manufacture of blended cements with a prefixed quantity of pozzolana or slags lower than this optimum, the flexibility to add larger doses becomes restricted. A major thrust area of R&D in NCB is toward evaluating blended cements for use with reactive aggregates as well as the development of newer cement compositions which, upon hydration, release little or no calcium hydroxide [Ca(OH)$_2$]. Fuller results of these investigations will be published later.

Conclusions

Results of periodic surveys show that the quality of cements in India has remained remarkably stable over the last three decades even in the face of increased production from a greater number of plants and a decline in the qualities of raw materials and fuel. To take into account the variability in the characteristics of cements used at a construction site, rapid methods of concrete mix adjustments are employed. Blended cements like portland pozzolana cement and portland slag cements, although having about 10% lower compressive strengths up to 28 days than ordinary portland cements from the same clinker, satisfy the minimum strength requirements with wide margins. Except for the availability of low tricalcium aluminate (C_3A) and low-alkali cements, which are somewhat restricted, the performance requirements of concrete constructions are adequately met.

Acknowledgments

This paper is based on the data available with the NCB Centre for Standardisation, Calibration, Testing and Quality Control (CTQ). S. Laxmi and K. H. Babu, scientists of the Centre, helped in the analyses of results.

References

[1] *Cement Standards of the World,* SP-1, 6th ed., Cement Research Institute of India, New Delhi, 1984.
[2] Visvesvaraya, H. C., *Cement,* Vol. 1, No. 4, July 1968, pp. 8–20.
[3] "Fixing the 28-Day Strength Limit of Cement Under Co-operative Testing Programme," *CRI Report* TG-211, Cement Research Institute of India, New Delhi, 1978.
[4] Mullick, A. K., Babu, K. H., and Rao, P. B., "Evaluation of Pozzolanic Activity and Its Impact on Specification of Blended Cements," 8th International Congress on the Chemistry of Cement, Rio de Janeiro, Brazil, 22-27 Sept. 1986, *Proceedings,* Vol. VI, pp. 308–311.
[5] Mullick, A. K., Iyer, S. R. and Babu, K. H., "Variability in Cements and Adjustments in Concrete Mixes by Accelerated Tests," 1983 International Concrete Congress, European Ready Mixed Concrete Organisation (ERMCO), Tauhallenstrasse, West Germany, London, May 1983.
[6] Visvesvaraya, H. C. and Mullick, A. K., "Developmental Efforts in Relation to Concrete Constructions in India," a state-of-art report, ACI's fall convention, New York, 1984, American Concrete Institute, Detroit, MI.

Mohammed S. Taryal[1] and M. K. Chowdhury[1]

Variability of Cement Strength in Saudi Arabia

REFERENCE: Taryal, M. S. and Chowdhury, M. K., **"Variability of Cement Strength in Saudi Arabia,"** *Uniformity of Cement Strength, ASTM STP 961,* E. Farkas and P. Klieger, Eds., American Society for Testing and Materials, Philadelphia, 1987, pp. 80–92.

ABSTRACT: The variability of cement strength depends mainly on the method of test and on the quality control of the cement production. Process changes, particularly in burning and cooling, may significantly alter the crystal structure and the strength development [8]. This study was conducted to determine the variation in cement strength due to variation in the test procedures adopted in Saudi standards as compared with other standards, and to study the variability of cement strength due to quality control of production in the individual company as well as between the eight cement companies of Saudi Arabia. The periodical cement samples from the cement companies were tested for fineness and compressive strength. The test data were analyzed statistically, and this shows the frequencies and sizes of apparent changes in process parameters such as mean, standard deviation, and coefficient of variation [10]. The quality of cement produced by individual companies is uniform and satisfies the minimum requirements according to Saudi Standard SSA 143/1979 and ASTM Specification for Portland Cement (C 150-85a), although there are different grades of production among the cement companies. The results reported in this study revealed the apparent quality and variability of cement strength in Saudi Arabia.

KEY WORDS: variability, compressive strength, quality, sample, mean, standard deviation coefficient of variation, acceptable limits

During recent years, there has been tremendous growth in the cement industry in Saudi Arabia due to the availability of raw materials in this country and to the huge cement demand. At present, eight cement companies distributed over Saudi Arabia (Fig. 1) are producing cement to meet just part of the country's demand.

The first cement company in Saudi Arabia was established in Jeddah in 1959 with an initial production capacity of 83.5 thousand tons/year. The second cement company was established in Haffouf in 1961 with an initial production capacity of 96 thousand tons/year [6]. Gradually, due to the increase in demand, not only did these two cement companies extend their production capacity, but also five new cement companies were established in Riyadh, Gassim, Yanbu, Zizan, and Upcake by the year 1982. Another cement company was established in Al-Khafzi in 1985. At present, the cement companies of Saudi Arabia are producing about 10 million tons/year [11].

Cement used as a structural material depends primarily on its strength, which plays an important role in determining its quality [9]. Every specification of cement requires a certain minimum compressive strength that must be attained under given conditions.

The aim of this paper is to study the variability of the values of compressive strength due to test procedures and due to quality control of products by the different cement companies of Saudi Arabia.

---

[1]Head and civil engineer, respectively, Building Research Department, Saudi Arabian Standards Organization, P.O. Box 3437, Riyadh 11471, Saudi Arabia.

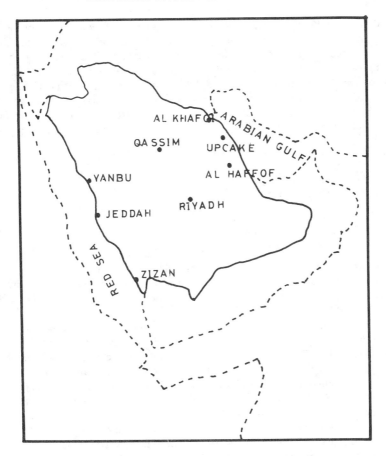

FIG. 1—*Location of cement companies.*

Variability of Strength Due to Test Procedure

The value of the compressive strength of cement is greatly influenced by testing procedures and conditions. Different countries have adopted different test procedures for determining the compressive strength of cement; accordingly, the Saudi Arabian Standards Organization (SASO) has issued Saudi Standard No. SSA 142/1979 [1], "Physical and Mechanical Testing Methods of Portland Cement."

An international joint test on cement with the same sample was carried out by the Cement Association of Japan in 1973. According to test results, it was observed that if the compressive strength at 3 days is 100 according to the ISO-REILEM test R-679 [2], the corresponding lowest strength of the same cement samples was observed to be 75 by ASTM Test Method for Compressive Strength of Hydraulic Cement Mortars (Using 2-in. or 50-mm Cube Specimens) (C 109-80) and the highest was observed to be 208 by the Greek standards test method. Similarly, if the value of compressive strength at 7 and 28 days is 100 by the ISO-REILEM test, the corresponding lowest strength of the same sample was observed to be 72 and 69, respectively, for 7 and 28 days by ASTM C 109-80, and if the highest value of compressive strength at 7 and 28 days is 100 by the ISO-REILEM test, the corresponding lowest strength of the same sample was observed to be 72 and 69, respectively, for 7 and 28 days by ASTM C 109, and the highest value of strength was observed to be 173 and 138, respectively, for 7 and 28 days by the Switzerland standard test method SIA 115. The just-cited test results show a large dispersion, which can be presumed to be due to the lack of unification of the test process, apparatus, and other details. It should be recognized that exact agreement cannot be secured by existing test methods by different operators or by the same operator at different times, even when the tests are made on the same sample under the same conditions [10]. Many steps are involved in testing compressive strength of cement; as a result, the value of compressive strength is sometimes greatly influenced by minor variations in procedure. A laboratory investigation was conducted to determine the variation of compressive strength by studying the following main steps in the procedure:

1. Mix proportion for mortars and water/cement (W/C) ratio.
2. Sand grading.
3. Method of mixing and compaction.
4. Shape and size of specimens.

Effect Due to Mix Proportions of Mortars and Water/Cement Ratio

The mix proportion of cement and sand is one of the main factors on which the value of compressive strength of cement depends. As such, all standards for testing cement have specified the mix proportions for the preparations of cement mortars. Table 1 shows the mix proportion of mortars according to the SSA, International Standards Organization (ISO), DIN (German), ASTM, and BS (British) standards.

The major variations in the test results may be expected to be due to the variation in the W/C ratio. The value of compressive strength of cement is an inverse function of the W/C ratio.

In order to study the effect of the W/C ratio on the value of compressive strength of cement, 264 mortar prism specimens of size 40 by 40 by 160 mm were prepared with different W/C ratios ranging from 0.40, 0.45, and 0.5 using standard sand according to SSA (143/1979), BS (12/1978 [5]) and ASTM Specification for Standard Sand (C 778-80a) standards following the test procedure according to SSA (143/1979) and tested at 28 days. Figure 2 shows the variation of compressive strength due to variation in W/C ratio and sand grading.

Figure 2 shows that compressive strength according to SSA/DIN/ISO produces a higher value than those values according to BS and ASTM standards due only to the variation of W/C ratio from 0.40 to 0.50; the value of compressive strength varies from about 60 to 47 N/mm^2, according to BS and ASTM. The value of compressive strength varies from about 73 to 60 N/mm^2 due to the variation of the W/C ratio from 0.4 to 0.5, according to SSA/DIN/ISO standards. This variation in compressive strength at the same W/C ratio may be mainly due to the sand grading, which has been varied in the test.

Effect Due to Sand Grading

The grading of sand used in mortars for standard tests has a significant effect on the value of compressive strength of cement. In some standards a sand of closely uniform size is used,

TABLE 1—*Mix proportion of mortars.*

Materials	\multicolumn{4}{c}{Mix Proportion (By Weight) According to Standard}
	SSA/ISO	DIN	ASTM	BS
Cement	1	1	1	1
Sand	3	3	2.75	3
Water/cement	0.5	0.5	0.485	0.4

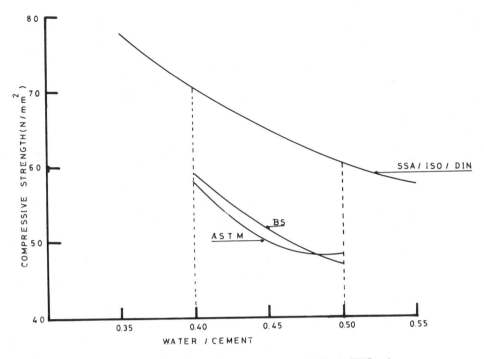

FIG. 2—*Values of compressive strength due to variation in W/C ratio.*

whereas some standards have specified a graded sand. In the British standard, the sand consists of round quartz grains passing BS No. 18 sieve (0.85 mm), with not more than 10% passing a No. 25 sieve (0.60 mm). In ASTM standard C 778-802 [4], a graded sand between ASTM No. 16 Sieve (1.19 mm) and ASTM No. 100 Sieve (0.149 mm) is used for the compressive strength test. In order to have uniformity among different countries in testing methods, an ISO-REILEM-CEMBUREAU method has been developed in which the test is carried out on a graded sand between 2 to 0.08 mm. The Saudi standard has adopted this graded sand. The particle size distribution of BS, ASTM, ISO, DIN 1164, and SSA are shown in Fig. 3.

In order to study the effect of compressive strength on sand grading, 72 number mortar prism specimens have been prepared using different standard sand according to Saudi, British, and ASTM standards (by the procedure according to the Saudi Standard SSA 142/1979) and have been tested at 28 days. Table 2 shows the test results of minimum, maximum, average, range, standard deviation, and coefficient of variation [7] of the value of the compressive strength of cement mortar due to the variation of sand grading.

Table 2 shows that the average value of compressive strength of cement mortar prepared with ISO/SSA sand is 60.28 N/mm², whereas the average value of compressive strength of the same cement mortar prepared with BS and ASTM sand is 47.81 and 46.84 N/mm², respectively. This shows that the value of compressive strength of the same cement varies from 46.84 to 60.28 N/mm², that is, there is about 25% variation in values of compressive strength due only to the quality of sand used for preparing mortar. The highest compressive strength obtained with the Saudi/ISO standard sand is due to the presence of a coarse particle size (2 mm), which is absent in the British and the ASTM standard sand. The standard deviation of the test results according to the Saudi standards is 2.94 N/mm², which is the highest when compared with those results of BS and the ASTM standards, although the SSA/ISO standard sand is available commercially

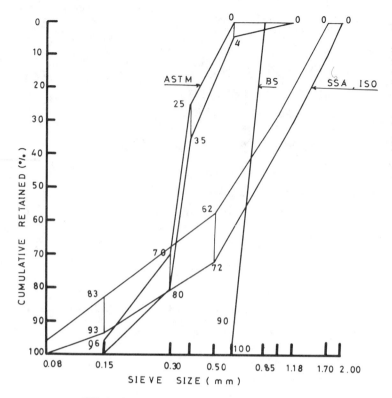

FIG. 3—*Particle size distribution of standard sand.*

TABLE 2—*Value of compressive strength due to sand grading.*

Items	Value of Compressive Strength at 28 days According to:		
	SSA/ISO	BS	ASTM
X min	50.56	46.03	44.80
X max	66.18	49.31	49.04
X av	60.28	47.81	46.84
R	15.22	3.28	4.24
S	2.94	1.64	1.62
Coefficient of variation, %	4.88	3.43	3.46

in small bags of 1350 g, which is sufficient for preparing three mortar prisms at a time, whereas the BS and the ASTM standard sand is available commercially in bags of 50 kg. The high dispersion of test results by the Saudi standards may be due to the presence of more fine and coarse particles than used with BS and the ASTM standards.

Effect of Due to Mixing Method

The object of mixing is simply to coat the surface of all aggregate particles with cement paste and to blend all the ingredients into a uniform mass. In order to attain this, in all standards the type of mixer, mixer blade revolution, blade planetary movement, mixing time, and sequence of feeding the ingredients into the mixer, etc., are all specified. Table 3 shows the sequence of mixing mortar by the different standards.

Table 3 shows that according to all the standards, for example, SSA/ISO, DIN, and ASTM, the cement paste, consisting of water and cement, is mixed first and then sand is added. After mixing the mortar, it is allowed to settle for 90 s, according to SSA/ISO and ASTM standards, whereas, according to DIN standards, settling time is allowed, rather the mortar is mixed continuously. According to British standards, the mixing is done by hand with two trowels for 300 s.

In order to study the effect of mixing time on the value of compressive strength, 72 mortar prism specimens have been prepared by mixing according to the SSA/ISO standard, which is the same as ASTM standard and DIN standard by holding other variables constant according to SSA. The test results of minimum, maximum, average, range, standard deviation, and coefficient of variation are shown in Table 4.

Table 4 shows that the value of compressive strength of mortar mixed according to DIN standards is 6% higher than the cement mortar mixed according to the SSA/ISO/ASTM standard. The standard deviation and the coefficient of variation of the test results are found to be 2.35 N/mm^2 and 3.72%, respectively, for the mortars mixed according to DIN standards, the values

TABLE 3—*Methods of mixing by different standards.*

| Items | Mixing Method According to: | | | |
	SSA/ISO	DIN	ASTM	BS
Sequence of feeding	Water and cement sand added	Water and cement added only		Mixing by hand, Mortar for each cube is mixed separately. Cement and dry sand is mixed for 60 s by two trowels, then water is added and mixed for 240 s with two trowels
Mixing at low speed	30 s			
Mixing at low speed	While sand added during 30 s	30 s While sand added during 30 s		
Mixing at high speed	30 s	60 s	30 s	
Stopping time	90 s	No	90 s	
Mixing at high speed	60 s	No	60 s	
Total time	240 s	120 s	240 s	300 s

TABLE 4—*Value of compressive strength due to mixing method.*

| Items | 28 Days Strength of Mortar Mixed by Method | |
	SSA/ISO/ASTM	DIN
X min	54.27	58.99
X max	63.91	67.28
X av	59.51	63.17
R	9.64	8.29
S	2.37	2.35
Coefficient of variation	3.98	3.72

of which are less than for those mortars mixed according to the SSA/ISO/ASTM standard. The lower values of the standard deviation and the coefficient of variation show more homogeneous test results, which may have occurred due to the mixing technique adopted by the DIN standard, where the cement paste is mixed first and then the cement paste is mixed with the sand continuously without stopping. This mixing technique may have produced more homogeneous mixes than the mixing technique of the SSA/ISO/ASTM standards.

Effect Due to Compaction Method

Compacting consists of expelling entrapped air and repositioning the aggregate particles in a dense state without causing segregation. Usually compaction is done either by manual method or by mechanical method. In all the standards, the type of vibrator, vibrating time, sequence of vibration, etc., are all specified. According to the Saudi standards, a mechanical vibrating table is used that vibrates only in the vertical direction at a frequency of 3000 rpm and at an amplitude of 0.75 mm. The compaction is done in two layers, each layer being compacted for 60 s. According to DIN standards, the same vibrating table is used, but the compaction is performed for 2 min continuously, mortar being charged into two layers. According to ISO standards, the compaction is achieved by a jolting table with a cam to fall freely from 15 mm at a speed of 1 rps, and the mortar is compacted in two layers, each layer being compacted for 60 jolts in 60 s. According to British standards, a mechanical vibrator having an out-of-balance moment of eccentric shaft of 0.016 Nm and a shaft speed of 1200 rpm is used for compacting the mortar cube specimens in one layer by vibrating for 2 min. According to ASTM standards, the compaction is done by hand with a tamping rod of cross section 2.54 by 1.27 cm (1 by $^1/_2$ in.) and 12.7 to 15.24 cm (5 to 6 in.) long. The compaction is done in two layers, each layer being compacted by tamping 32 times in 10 s.

In order to study the effect of the compaction method on the value of compressive strength, 72 mortar prism specimens have been prepared by compacting according to SSA and DIN standards by holding the other variables constant according to Saudi standards. The test results of minimum, maximum, average, range, standard deviation, and the coefficient of variation are shown in Table 6, from which it is noted that there is no significant difference in the value of compressive strength due to the difference in the method of compaction. The range, standard deviation, and the coefficient of variation were found to be nearly the same between the two methods of compaction.

Effect Due to Shape and Size of Specimens

Different standards have adopted a different size and shape for the mortar specimens. The Saudi, ISO, and DIN standards have adopted prism specimens 40 by 40 by 160 mm. The value

TABLE 5—*Value of compressive strength due to compaction method.*

Items	28-Day Strength by Compaction Method According to:	
	SSA/ISO	DIN
X min, N/mm^2	53.82	50.54
X max, N/mm^2	66.57	64.21
X av, N/mm^2	61.40	60.35
R, N/mm^2	12.75	13.67
S, N/mm^2	4.27	4.12
Coefficient of variation	6.95	6.83

of compressive strength is evaluated on the broken halves of the specimens broken in flexure on one of the lateral moulded faces, whereas, according to British standards, tests are made on 70.7-mm-cube specimens. In the ASTM standard, prism specimens (40 by 40 by 160 mm) and cube specimens (50 mm) are used to determine the value of the compressive strength of cement. In general, it is known that the larger the specimen, the lower the indicated strength. As such, some minor variation in the test results may be expected due to a different shape and size of the specimens adopted by the different standards.

Variability of Strength Due to Quality Control of the Production

The variability of compressive strength of cement is greatly influenced by the composition and proportions of raw materials, as well as by the manufacturing process. About 95% of cement clinker is made of certain compounds of four oxides: lime, silica, alumina, and iron, with other minor constituents such as magnesium, sodium, and potassium oxides and titanium, sulfur, phosphorus, and manganese oxides [8].

In order to study the variability of the value of compressive strength due to quality control of production, 84 samples of cement were collected from seven cement companies over a period of three months of production representing one sample each week comprised of seven subsamples of 10 kg each from every day's production. The following tests were performed on each of the samples:

1. Chemical analysis.
2. Fineness test.
3. Compressive strength at different ages of 1, 3, 7, and 28 days.

Chemical Analysis

For each sample of cement, silicon dioxide (SiO_2), calcium oxide (CaO), magnesium oxide (MgO), ferrous oxide (Fe_2O_3), aluminum oxide (Al_2O_3), and sulfur trioxide (SO_3), loss on ignition and insoluble residue were determined, and the major chemical compounds were calculated, according to ISO R-680 [3].

Fineness

The fineness of each sample of cement was determined according to Saudi Standard SSA/142/1979, by the Blaine Air Permeability method ASTM Test Method for Fineness at Portland Cement by Air Permeability Apparatus (C 204-84) [4]. The minimum (X min), maximum (X max), average (X), and range (R) of the values of fineness of all the cement companies are shown in Table 6. Figures 4 and 5 show the results of statistical analysis of the values of fineness of cement samples of each cement company.

Table 6 shows that the minimum fineness is 2777 cm^2/g (Company 7) and that the maximum fineness is 3977 cm^2/g (Company 2). Figure 4 shows that there are several levels of fineness. The lowest level of production for fineness of cement is by Company 7, followed by Companies 1, 4, 5, and 3. The highest level of production for fineness is by Company 2.

Figure 5 shows that all the cement companies have good quality control for the fineness of cement. The standard deviations are 32, 47, 53, 62, 64, 69, and 70 cm^2/g for Companies 2, 3, 5, 1, 6, 7, and 4, respectively. In spite of the different levels of quality control for the fineness of cement, in general the levels are of acceptable quality, although the variation in fineness is quite high. Although there is a big scattering of the values of fineness, these values satisfy the requirements for the Saudi Standard Specification SSA 143/1979, where the minimum standard limit is 2250 cm^2/g for all types of cement.

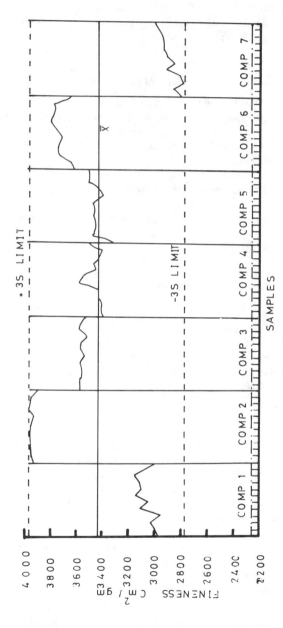

FIG. 4—Control chart for fineness of cement samples of all cement companies.

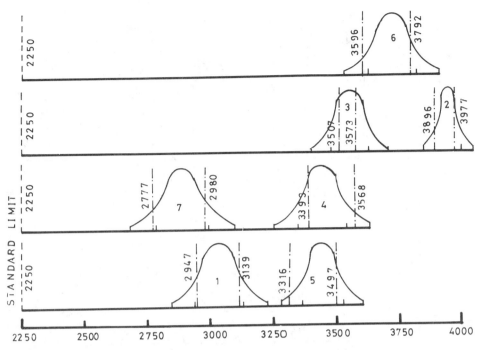

FIG. 5—*Fineness of cement of all cement companies.*

TABLE 6—*Fineness of cement.*

| Cement Co. | Fineness of Cement, cm^2/g | | | |
	Minimum	Maximum	Mean	Range
No. 1	2947	3139	3040	192
No. 2	3896	3977	3947	81
No. 3	3509	3573	3547	64
No. 4	3393	3568	3448	175
No. 5	3316	3497	3445	181
No. 6	3596	3792	3719	196
No. 7	2777	2980	2887	203

Compressive Strength

The compressive strength of cement mortar was determined by prism specimens 40 by 40 by 160 mm. From each sample, three prism specimens were prepared simultaneously for testing at different ages of 1, 3, 7, and 27 days. The mortar is composed of 1 part cement and 3 parts by weight of standard sand complying with the requirements of Saudi Standard SSA 142/1979. It is worthwhile to mention here that, before conducting the tests, the precision of the laboratory of SASO was determined and was found to be within one sigma limit [13]. Table 8 shows the test results for the value of minimum (X min), maximum (X max), average (X), and range (R) of compressive strength of all the cement samples of all the cement companies at specified ages. Figure 6 shows the results of the statistical analysis of cement strength at different ages for the samples of all the cement companies.

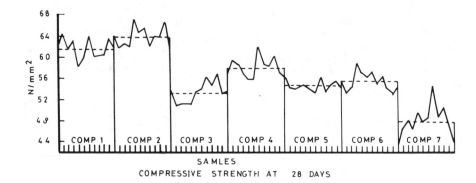

COMPRESSIVE STRENGTH AT 28 DAYS

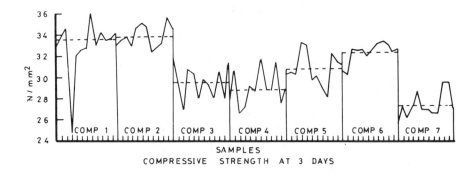

COMPRESSIVE STRENGTH AT 7 DAYS

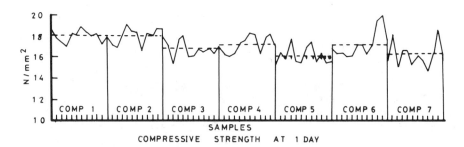

FIG. 6—*Control chart for compressive strength of cement samples of all cement companies.*

Table 7 shows that there are several levels of strength. The level of strength of Cement Companies 1 and 2 are nearly the same, since the mean value of compressive strength at 28 days is 61.61 and 63.67 N/mm², respectively. Company 4 shows the second level of strength, the mean value of compressive strength at 28 days being 57.80 N/mm². Companies 3, 5, and 6 show the third level of strength, having the mean value of compressive strength of 53.09, 54.58, and 55.48 N/mm², respectively. Company 7 shows the fourth level of strength, the mean value of compressive strength at 28 days being 47.87 N/mm².

Table 8 shows the value of the standard deviation for the test results, from which it is evident that all the cement companies have fairly good quality control over the product. The best quality control of the product exits in Company 5, since the value of standard deviation at different ages ranges between 0.908 to 1.704 N/mm², which is quite low and shows homogeneity of the product. The second best quality control system exists in Company 6. The value of the standard deviation ranges between 0.946 and 1.783 N/mm². Third is Company 3, as far as quality control is concerned. The value of the standard deviation ranges between 0.815 and 2.038 N/mm² at different ages, the mean value being 1.44 N/mm². Fourth is Company 2.

TABLE 7—*Compressive strength of cement.*

Age, Days	Designation	Compressive Strength for Cement Company No:						
		1	2	3	4	5	6	7
1	Minimum	14.27	16.47	15.29	16.11	15.18	16.05	14.76
	Maximum	18.93	19.15	18.07	18.33	17.82	20.05	18.73
	Range	4.66	2.68	2.78	2.22	2.64	4.00	3.97
	Mean	17.74	18.02	16.81	17.19	16.10	17.20	16.26
3	Minimum	24.55	32.25	26.89	26.40	28.05	30.10	25.59
	Maximum	35.82	35.72	32.10	31.77	33.38	33.47	29.54
	Range	11.27	3.48	5.21	5.37	5.33	3.37	3.95
	Mean	32.81	33.88	29.52	28.86	30.78	32.37	27.29
7	Minimum	37.87	45.13	36.50	37.88	40.25	42.46	33.20
	Maximum	53.63	51.61	41.03	44.83	46.25	48.96	38.66
	Range	15.76	6.48	4.53	6.95	6.00	5.60	5.46
	Mean	47.58	48.36	38.34	40.83	44.03	44.81	36.07
28	Minimum	58.10	60.68	50.52	55.47	53.23	52.93	42.93
	Maximum	65.54	67.17	56.85	61.99	56.32	58.82	54.76
	Range	6.44	6.49	6.33	6.52	3.09	5.89	11.83
	Mean	61.61	63.67	53.09	57.80	54.58	55.48	47.87

TABLE 8—*Standard deviation for compressive strength.*

Company No.	Standard Deviation for Compressive Strength, days, N/mm²			
	1	3	7	28
1	1.216	2.802	4.205	1.993
2	0.793	1.089	2.077	2.062
3	0.815	1.566	1.342	2.038
4	0.843	1.609	2.159	1.976
5	0.908	1.554	1.704	0.908
6	1.319	0.946	1.456	1.783
7	1.207	1.200	1.618	3.071

The value of the standard deviation ranges between 0.783 to 2.077 N/mm^2 at different ages. Then Companies 4, 7, and 1 have the next degree of quality control. In general, it may be concluded that there is an acceptable quality control level in all the cement companies, although the level of quality control differs from one company to another.

By comparing the test results with Saudi standards, it is evident that the cement samples conform to the requirements of Saudi standards, although there is a big difference between the limit specified in the standards and the actual compressive strength; as such, it may be necessary to increase the minimum limit for the compressive strength, which will make present production more economic and will allow natural raw materials to be utilized efficiently.

Conclusions and Recommendations

An evaluation of the data of this study leads to the following recommendations:

1. The standard deviation of test results of mortar prisms prepared by the uniformly graded standard British and American sand is lower than that of the mortar prisms prepared by the well-graded SSA/ISO standard sand.

2. Since there is no significant effect on the strength value due to different methods of mixing and compaction of mortar prism specimens, the simple method of mixing and compaction according to DIN may be recommended.

3. The general level of quality control of the product for all Saudi Arabian cement companies is high.

4. There are different levels of cement strength in each cement company, which allows for a choice of cement having suitable compressive strength for different construction purposes.

5. Considering the actual quality of the product, it is essential to revise present Saudi standards by increasing the minimum limit for compressive strength to utilize the product more economically.

References

[1] Saudi Standard SSA 142/1979, "Physical and Mechanical Testing Methods of Portland Cement."
[2] ISO Recommendation R-679, "Method of Testing Strength of Cements, Compressive and Flexural Strengths of Plastic Mortar," 1st ed., March 1968.
[3] ISO Recommendation R-680, "Chemical Analysis of Cements Main Constituents of Portland Cement," 1st ed., 1968.
[4] American Standards: ASTM Standard Specification for Portland Cement (C 150-85a); ASTM Method for Chemical Analysis of Hydraulic Cement (C 114-85); ASTM Specification for Standard Sand (C 778-80a) ASTM Test Methods for Fineness of Portland Cement by Air Permeability Apparatus (C 204-84).
[5] British Standards: BS 12/1978 "Portland Cement, Ordinary and Rapid Hardening"; BS 12/1971 "Portland Cement, Ordinary and Rapid Hardening"; BS 12/1958 "Portland Cement, Ordinary and Rapid Hardening."
[6] Al-Turki, A. M. and McCullough, J., "Analysis of Cement Demand in Saudi Arabia," *Proceedings, IAHS International Conference, 1978, on Housing Problems in Developing Countries,* Vol. 2, John Wiley & Sons, New York.
[7] Juran, J. M., Seder, L. A., and Gryna, Jr. F. M., *Quality Control Handbook,* 2nd ed., McGraw-Hill, New York.
[8] Lea, F. M., *The Chemistry of Cement and Concrete,* 3rd ed., Edward Arnold.
[9] Popovics, S., *Concrete Making Materials,* McGraw-Hill, New York, 1979.
[10] Grant, E. L., and Leavenworth, R. S., *Statistical Quality Control,* 4th ed., McGraw-Hill, New York.
[11] Arab Union for Cement and Building Materials, "Cement Data Book."
[12] Taryal, M. S., and Chowdhury, M. K., "Evaluation of Relation Between Compressive Strength of Cement by the British Standard Cube Test and ISO Reliem Prism Test," *International Journal for Cement and Concrete Research,* Vol. 2, 1982.
[13] Taryal, M. S. and Chowdhury, M. K., "Determination of Precision of Cement Testing Laboratories," *SASO Standard Magazine,* No. 2, 1982.
[14] The Cement Association of Japan, "Report on Examples of Joint Test of Cement at Abroad," 15 Sept. 1973.

Subject Index

Author Index